I REMEMBER WHEN

THE COLLECTION

BY ARNOLD FINE

In memory of Mama and Papa and everyone
else who's memory will always be kept alive by
these "I Remember When" stories.

DEDICATION

To my darling wife Edith — my three sons,
Jay, Brian and Martin my daughters-in-law
Cindy, Dina and Janet and my grandchildren
Eric, Daniel, Joan, and Sarah.

Table of Contents

A NOTE FROM THE AUTHOR

I have been writing these *I Remember When* stories for *The Jewish Press* for the past 43 years. I treasure the thousands of wonderful letters I received over the years. I will never forget the one I got from a nurse, "Bless you, Mr. Fine! Your stories are the best medicine my patients have ever received."

A doctor once wrote, "I prescribe your stories to all my patients. I tell them to forget the pills, just take and read one *I Remember When* story each week. It cures everything!"

So, to all my friends, here's the collection of stories you asked for. If you enjoy these, let me know and maybe we could put together "*Son of I Remember When?*"

Arnold Fine

FOREWORD TO THE FIRST EDITION

By Harry Hershfield

I've worked with some of the leading comedians in show business over the years; some of the greatest radio and television comics who have become household words. But none comes close to the warmth and simple humor expressed in the *I Remember When* stories! The beauty of these stories is that you really don't have to be Jewish to enjoy them. I knew an Irish family, some years ago, whose experiences were almost the same as the family in I Remember When.

I once worked with a Negro entertainer who, when he read one of the stories thought that Arnold Fine must have planted a microphone in his home. He swore his experiences were almost the same.

I have run across Italian, Greek and Scottish friends, who after reading an *I Remember When* story all agreed that these stories were a very real part of their lives, too.

This collection of stories is a treasure. With the printed word of *I Remember When* at your side, you are never alone.

Mr. Fine shares his family with all of us. His mother and father are universal.

Arnie Fine is not living in the past. He brings the past to us, capturing the truth of the years gone by. With his uncanny ability he makes these memories sound as if they just had happened. The situations, the idioms and the warmth of every story makes you a part of the story and you feel as if you are reading about your own childhood.

I've shared the same page with Arnold Fine in THE JEWISH PRESS for twelve years and I must admit the first thing I do is to turn to the back of the paper each week to see if I'm still employed and then proceed to read *I Remember When.*

I am so pleased to be given this space to add my few words of appreciation to Arnold Fine for helping to brighten my life. Let this volume be among the little treasures of our history, because it says so much, so simply.

Harry Hershfield

(Ed. note: Harry Hershfeld wrote this introduction for the first printing of I Remember When. After he wrote it, he called and said he wished he could have ten pages because he loved those stories so much. A few days later, Harry passed away. This was the last thing he had written.)

INTRODUCTION

I'll never forget the day the *I Remember When* stories were born. As the Editor of *The Jewish Press*, I was turning in copy for an issue. Earlier that day, I had written a three page schmooz letter to a friend. In the confusion of getting the copy to the linotype machines, pages two and three of the letter got caught in the pile of typewritten material.

I'll never forget that night! Two linotype machines broke down, there a was a power failure, and it was snowing! We were so late, it was an even money bet whether the paper would even be printed that night.

When they brought me the page proofs, I just scanned them and rushed them through. We had trucks waiting for the paper and the press crew was screaming – *nu* – so what was I to do – sit and start reading page proofs?

The paper went to press. As the first copy rolled off, I settled down to see how bad it was. After all, it wasn't the best paper that week, but it was out – and that was the important thing.

When I reached page 18 I almost dropped dead! There

it was - pages two and three of my letter to Herby. The make-up man took the first three words of my letter which began, "I remember when..." put it in headline type and put my name under the heading.

I figured, maybe nobody would notice. Who would be interested in me writing to a friend about "the good old days."

Oy, did they notice! The following week we started getting mail, everyone started writing in about the things they remembered from their youth.

I was asked to write another "column" of "I Remember When." I tried and it started to write itself. I continued writing the column week after week. It became a labor of love. Listen, how many of us could talk about our family and even get paid for it?

That's how it began.

Did all these things really happen to me or my family? The truth is, about 99% is fact. Maybe 1% is fiction and that fiction lies in the fact that I have not used the actual names of those I remember so well.

As I began to write more and more stories touching on the nostalgia of yesterday's world, a dear old friend, Harry Hershfield, called me one day and said he enjoyed the stories more than anything he had ever read. Harry was the Dean of American Humorists, a man who entertained millions over the years. He would call me each week and ask me to read the column going into print.

"When you write the book," Harry said, "I want to write the foreword!"

I was so pleased. Then when the book was being put together, Harry sent me his foreword. He passed away a few days later. It was one of the last things he wrote.

In a sense of humility I hesitated to include it in the volume. However, everyone who has been connected with the production of this book felt that Harry's words should be part of the story.

Arnold Fine

WHAT USED TO BE...

Whatever happened to the things we enjoyed as kids that were just around the corner? Today, to get the same enjoyment you may have to travel to Disneyworld in Florida.

EMEMBER THOSE WARM SPRING AND SUM-mer nights how a ride on an open trolly was a pleasure? For a big five cents you could ride the open air trolly for hours. It was like a land cruise, sort of the poor man's expedition. We rode through the neighborhoods and saw all kinds of people doing their thing.

Today, if you want an open air trolly ride, you're out of luck.

Let me ask you, wouldn't it be nice if they built a trolly system along the Belt Parkway in Brooklyn? We could take a cool ride during those hot summer months? We could drink in the soothing evening breezes along the parkway.

Remember the good old summer time when we could go to the beach in Rockaway or Coney Island and enjoy the surf and the sand? Today, when we go to the beach we have a new pastime. We count syringes and medical waste! And boy-o-boy do you have to watch what you walk on! If the medical waste doesn't get you the oil sludge and tar will.

Remember those wonderful lazy days as a kid where a big night was simply sitting on the stoop or the steps in front of the house and just talking baseball. Or, maybe playing some of the word games we played in those years. Remember the games actors and actresses? Remember that one? In our day actors and actresses are so well known all you had to do was mention their initials and everyone knew immediately who you were thinking of. The only time the game got tough was when someone used the initials of some obscure bit player.

We would play another game called GHOST. Remember that game? Someone would name a letter in the alphabet. Then, someone else would say another letter and so on. If the word was completed by the time it reached the fourth or fifth player, they got a 'G.' If the words kept coming out on that person you added an 'H' and then an 'O' and then an 'S' and finally a 'T.' If the word GHOST came out on a player, he or she was out of the game. As a matter of fact most of us sharpened our spelling skills with that game.

Remember those real hot days when an iceman's truck would come down the street and the iceman would throw us a little chunk of ice to suck on so we could keep cool?

Those were the wonderful days when you could walk in the park and enjoy the birds and the trees. It was delightful. Today, if you want to go to the park you literally need a Sherman Tank!

If you wanted to go to an amusement park in our day you went to Coney Island or Rockaway's Playland. Today, of course there are still some rides in Coney Island, but

Rockaway's Playland is long gone. True, you may have to mortgage your house to pay for a ride on one of today's amusement attractions, but the thrill is still there.

For culture in our day, we would visit the foreign pavilions at the World's Fair. Each pavilion was like entering a new world. The attendants wore the colorful costumes of that nation and the art and culture of that part of the world was displayed all over the place.

In our day, the World's Fair was an oasis of entertainment. I remember buying a booklet of tickets in school and for about a dollar we would go to the Fair on those hot summer days and enjoy the cool air-conditioning they had in each exhibit.

I remember how thrilled I was seeing my first television set at the RCA exhibit at the World's Fair in Flushing Meadows. We stood in line for hours before they let us in. When we finally got to the exhibit hall they ushered us into a smaller darkened room with a big box at the end of the room. The box contained a television tube that carried a picture being televised from another section of the building. Wow, was that thrilling! And I remember so many people who were in line with us laughing, "That's just an electronic fad. It will never last."

When the demonstrator said, "These sets will be available within the next few years for only a thousand dollars." We sighed and felt - "...well forget it - this is strictly for the rich."

Color television was absolutely unheard of in those days. From time to time there were stories in magazines that told about experiments with color television. We laughed, "It's difficult enough to send a picture through the air - now they're gonna send color pictures! This is real craziness."

The announcer in the exhibit said, "We are on the threshold of a new world."

And we were!

Today they're talking about this new invention called High Definition Color Television. This is supposed to be a television set that brings in a picture so sharp it looks as if it were a photograph. They say such a set will cost about $3,000 when they are released commercially. Again we turn away and feel our little black and white set is just as good – besides who doesn't have something better to do with $3,000? Will they show better programs? *Ver vais?*

I think the exhibit that sparked my imagination the most in those years was the General Electric exhibit called, 'Steinmetz Hall.' Remember that exhibit where they had two bare ominous looking metal towers. You would hear a surge of electricity as they would put thousands of volts of electricity into those towers. Then suddenly there would be a tremendous explosion as a shot of lightning would flash from one tower to the other. Those who waited to see the demonstration would wait for hours to see the actual man-made lightning blast that took less than a second. But it was worth it.

The General Motors exhibit was also one you had to stand in line for at least two hours. When you finally got to the entrance to the exhibit they sat you in a little neatly upholstered chair that rode along a track and showed you the 'World of Tomorrow.' They told you how people would be living in the 1980's and we were flabbergasted with the innovations they promised us in the future.

In another exhibit, and I just forgot the name, they said people would be living underground in a temperature controlled environment in the 1980's. This exhibit was underground. There were windows that had lights and projected pictures on the wall to give the effect of winter, summer, spring and fall. They told you to simply press a button and you could enjoy any season of the year. The lights in the room would change and the room would get cold or warm depending on what season you pressed. If you pressed Spring you also got the scent of fresh flowers and grass.

There was also the huge Billy Rose Aquacade where young men and women would swim in a gigantic pool to soft ballet music. The swimmers would do precision water ballets on top and under the water. What a thrilling sight that was!

Then they had the show, "The Hot Mikado" with Bill Robinson. It was an all Black cast doing a modernized jazz version of the Gilbert and Sullivan opera, The Mikado. Today, we even have a sensational Mikado troop that does that Gilbert and Sullivan masterpiece in Yiddish! See what they started.

Some years ago they tried to duplicate a sort of mini-World's Fair in the Bronx, but it didn't last too long. They called the place Freedomland. It had to close down for the severe winter months. Those closings really hurt the business. A real estate developer eventually bought the land and put up today what is known as Co-op City.

I wonder how many old timers can remember the big song in our generaton? Remember, "The Music Goes Round and Round"? That song was played on every radio station for about six weeks. They played it maybe ten or twenty times a day. The lyrics were silly and told of music going round and round in a french horn. A real *narishkiet!*

Today, the music sounds like some garbage men dumping cans into a truck and the lyrics are simply sick. In fact, so many people attribute a good deal of the violence in today's world to some of the sick and stupid Rock lyrics the kids listen to.

Listen, it's a new world.

INSTANT COMMUNICATIONS

As much as the world of communication has advanced – it still hasn't caught up to the "instant" news media we had in our day.

L ET ME TELL YOU SOMETHING, IF ANYTHING IN our immediate neighborhood ever happened – you could find out instantly by going into the corner candy store for a two cents glass of plain seltzer. Mrs. Grodefsky was the "News Bulletin" of our day – a walking newspaper. If someone was going to have a baby – she knew three seconds after the mother knew. If someone was going to get married – she would know seconds after the proposal was made.

Listen – there wasn't much that Grodefsky didn't know! How? Why? Was she a noseybody? Of course not – all she did was work behind the counter making up sodas or two cents plain. But in those years – who in our neighborhood had a telephone? No one, except the corner candy store. So, if Mrs. Silverman got a phone call at the candy store and a doctor would say that her tests were positive – she would gasp, "Oy, doctor that's wonderful – my husband will be so happy!" Grodefsky knew already! If Selma Lieberman's boyfriend proposed over the telephone – when she left the booth she would hug and kiss Mrs. Grodefsky. She knew already what happened.

Nu – so how did she relay these instant "bulletins" to the neighborhood in general? Simple! If someone gave birth she would hang a little rubber doll in the store window. Everyone in the neighborhood knew her signals. If someone got engaged – two huge boxes of chocolates went into the window with a sign that read "*Mazel Tov!*" We knew – we knew – we didn't need newscasters.

If ever a hard news story broke – like when Mr. Barenholtz was arrested for punching his boss in the nose and was being held in the police station – the bulletin would go out in a special way. Usually she got the phone call for Mrs. Barenholtz with instructions to come down to the police station to bail out her husband. On such occasions dear old Mrs. Grodefsky would give one of us a penny to run up to Mrs. Barenholtz's apartment to tell her to go to the police station. We would run to the apartment house, stand in the hall at the bottom of the stairs and yell out "B-a-r-e-n-h-o-l-t-z! Mrs. Grodefsky says you should go to the police station to bail out your husband. He hit his boss."

Fifteen doors would suddenly open and ten neighbors would join poor Mrs. Barenholtz in her pilgrimage to the police station. Let me tell you something – this Mr. Barenholtz was some character. He was a red hot Hungarian who was usually referred to as *Der Fabrendt'er* (the one who burns – actually hot-head). If ever there was an argument in the building you can bet your bottom dollar Mr. Barenholtz was in the middle.

Saturday night being at the corner candy store was

almost a must. We would stand in front of the store from about seven o'clock in the evening on and wait for the 'date' calls to come in. Whenever a 'date' call came in, Mrs. Grodefsky would answer the phone in the following manner, "Hullah –" then she would pause. "Goldberg? Sarah Goldberg? Yeh – yeh –wait I'll call Sarah." Then she would motion to one of us; give us the building address and say, "Goldberg – call Sarah – her boyfriend – it's ah date...it's good for ah nickel tip. But yell loud!"

We would run to the designated house, stand in the hall and bellow, "Goldberg! Goldberg! Sarah Goldberg! Telephone! You're all set for tonight! It's your boyfriend."

Sarah would come charging down the stairs all smiles, press a nickel or sometimes a dime – and even on one occasion a quarter into our outstretched palm and race for the candy store on the corner.

Listen – it was a good business for Grodefsky too. If the date didn't stop by for the box of candy – the next time he would call we would get orders to call Sarah to the phone 'softly.' If we got no answer Grodefskey would say to the caller, "Sarah's date from last week must have taken her out already. He bought a big box of candy last week. Listen – where were you? – I had a box waiting for you!" The caller usually got the message – and the candy the following week – and Sarah got her calls.

When the army years came upon us – Grodefsky changed her window. She put up a big piece of cardboard and very neatly wrote on top of it in colored crayons "Serving Our Country." Underneath she would paste the pictures of the fellows who went into the service. All the guys in the neighborhood would send her pictures wherever they were in the world. In fact, a great many of them put her name and address down on the army papers where it asked who to notify in the event of an emergency. They knew Mrs. Grodefsky was the one to break the news to their parents if there was ever an emergency.

Listen – I don't have to tell you how fast bad news

travels – and *takeh* – it traveled. When the first kid on the block was reported missing in action – she saw the Western Union boy pull up on his bike in front of the house across the street from her store. In those years when you saw a Western Union boy – you knew already it was bad news. Who would send good news in a telegram? So Grodefsky knew! She would close the store and go up to the apartment where the telegram was delivered. From the screams you could hear in the hall – she knew already what the telegram contained. The picture of the boy that hung with the others in her window was bordered in black crayon that night. It really wasn't necessary – in our old neighborhood everybody knew already.

And then another telegram came – and then another – and within a very short period of time, the piece of cardboard that stood in her window had – maybe eight black bordered pictures. Our neighborhood did its part – all right!

After the war was over Mrs. Grodefsky took the cardboard out of her window and carefully took off the pictures of the boys who were lost in the war. She made up another cardboard and put a black border around it. She placed the eight pictures of the boys who were lost in the center – and every night for as long as I can remember – she had a *Yahrzeit* glass lit and placed it in front of the cardboard. It was her Eternal Light – for "her boys."

Come to think of it – she didn't have any children of her own. Her husband passed away shortly after they opened the candy store. She stood in that store from morning till night. It was her life. And as each kid was reported missing she literally sat shiva for each one. They were her children! Every one! In fact the kids would tell her things they couldn't tell their own parents. She wrote to everyone in her own inimitable style and always enclosed a stick of Wrigley's chewing gum – so that the kids should remember the old candy store on the corner.

The old lady kept that candy store for years – even after most of the people in the old neighborhood moved out. The

Puerto Rican youngsters who moved into the community continued to be 'her boys' and any time one of the kids would get in trouble she would be the first one at the police station, pleading for 'her kids.' They loved that old woman.

When she passed away I think that was the only time in history that more Puerto Rican people went to our old shul than Jews. They all went to pay tribute to that dear old lady. In that neighborhood, how many Jews were left? She had no immediate family – but there must have been at least a thousand people filling the streets as the hearse carried her to her final resting place.

Some who received word of her passing got together a short time ago and paid for perpetual care for her grave and placed a rather novel headstone on it. It was simple; it had a *Yahrzeit* glass carved into the stone – just like the one she put in her window every night. Underneath it simply said, "With her boys again."

I guess every neighborhood had a Mrs. Grodefsky – someone who became another parent. Someone who held a nervous hand, caressed a tortured soul, and soothed a broken heart.

THE ICE BOX SHISSEL

Everything in yesterday's world gave double service. For example, who can ever forget the ice box shissel?

HE ICE BOX *SHISSEL* WAS A LITTLE BASIN PLACED underneath the ice box to catch the drippings from the ice as it melted.

It didn't have to be a fancy pot - only serviceable. We had just such a pan and believe it or not, when Mama moved from the old place she still had that old ice box *shissel*, even though every apartment had a refrigerator.

"Waddya need the *shissel* for?" I questioned. "Just something else to shlep?"

"It's still serviceable! Mama exclaimed. "How much room does it take? You always have a need for ah *shissel*!"

And so we packed it up with the other kitchen wares.

But I'm getting ahead of myself – because that *shissel* had a personality all its own.

I remember when Mama first purchased that *shissel* in the hardware store. In those days it wasn't really a *shissel*, it was more of a deep pan with a handle.

In the beginning Mama used it to hard-boil eggs. It was a handsome pan, sort of a grey enamel. Maybe a thousand eggs we enjoyed with shav or borsht were boiled in that pan. And then as the years went by, and after a few thousand washings by my sisters, the pot became a little chipped. Then the handle snapped off. That was it! It was now a basin.

It was then sent out to pasture. How would it look to boil eggs in a chipped pan without a handle? No longer would it be filled with water and placed on the stove for the water to boil. It was relegated   to catching the drippings from the ice.

It wasn't a very large basin. You had to empty it three times a day.

I remember when we got up in the morning, the first thing we would do would be to run into the kitchen and take out the *shissel* to dump the accumulated water.

Some time during the afternoon, Mama would empty the *shissel* of the day's drippings, and before we went to sleep we would empty it a third time.

It was almost like having a pet to take care of – we had a regular schedule for emptying that *shissel*.

Sometimes, when we would forget, or if we went away for a whole day the *shissel* would overflow and run over onto the floor and then down into Mrs. Mermelstein's apartment below. We would find out when Mermelstein would bang on the ceiling with her broom and angrily shout up, " Mrs. Fine – *ess rint iber bei dir der shissel!*"

We would rush to the *shissel* and carefully work our way over to the sink to dump the water, but invariably we would be so nervous that we would manage to dump the greater part of the water on the floor – only to hear Mermelstein knock with her broom once more and shout,

"Mrs. Fine, it's getting high tide down here!"

Mama would come running with the mop she always kept on the fire escape and begin to swab the floor.

But the water continued to flow down to Mrs. Mermelstein's apartment since the water had a good headstart. In a few minutes Mrs. Mermelstein would be at our door banging away angrily. "Mrs. Fine – open up – *ess gist ah mahbil by mir!*" (It's pouring water by me!)

Mama would open the door sheepishly and bring Mermelstein into the freshly mopped kitchen that we quickly dried and tried to explain, "Only a little ran over – maybe it's a broken pipe – or maybe it's running from somebody else's apartment."

Mermelstein would leave – not completely convinced, but satisfied we had arrested the flood.

As the years passed, when an emergency came up and somebody sprained an ankle, the only deep pan we had in the house was the ice box *shissel*. So a soup bowl would be placed under the ice box and the shissel taken into the bathroom where Epsom salts and warm water were placed in it so that a foot could soak. I guess you could almost see that little *shissel* swell with pride – being able to serve humanity once more.

Sometimes, if Mama expected company and had to boil a large quantity of eggs, the *shissel* would be taken out once more, carefully scoured, and put into special service. How proudly it performed. And then when the cooking was over – it was put back under the ice box. It was always there when needed.

Then there were times when Mama was making a yeast cake and found that all her pans were being used and needed a deep pan to set near the stove for the dough to rise. That ice box *shissel* was washed very carefully and lined with brown paper. The dough was placed in it to rise. How proudly that little pan served once more.

And then the summer came and the family would go on the roof in those steaming hot nights, Mama would usually take the *shissel* out once more, fill it with cool water and place a few pieces of ice in it. Then she would put a few bottles of seltzer in the *shissel*. It became our "champagne cooler!" We would sit on the roof, drinking in the cool evening breezes and occasionally filling up a glass with cool seltzer. The evening over, the *shissel* would be placed back under the ice box.

And then when my sister's first child was born in our old house, and Mama needed something to keep the first diapers in until we could get a special container, the *shissel* also became a part of that new family. It was carefully washed once more and used to hold the soiled diapers. And the following day when a pure white porcelain container was purchased to hold the diapers, the *shissel* was returned to its primary duty, under the ice box.

And then when my younger sister got married and Mama needed something to carry the cookies and the cakes she made to the shul for a *kiddush*, the basin was removed from under the ice box, carefully washed and lined with wax paper and then filled with the goodies that were taken to shul. And how thrilled that little *shissel* must have been being a participant in so many personal and wonderful memories.

And I'll never forget the day a water main broke in the street and people had to run a block away to a fire hydrant to get water – the largest container we had in the house was that *shissel*. It brought back water for drinking and for cooking. It played a part in our survival.

And so when Mama left the old place and refrigerators replaced ice boxes, who needed a *shissel* that didn't even have a handle? But you just don't throw out an old friend. Mama kept the *shissel* in the laundry closet and used it to keep the clothespins in.

And then when they got to their new place, where there was a washing machine and a dryer in the building basement – of what use was it to keep that *shissel*? But still Mama wouldn't throw it out.

So she saved it all these years. Just the other day I needed a container to mix some soil so that I could plant a few tomato plants in the backyard and I really hated to go out and buy one of those fancy plastic basins - so when Mama called she suggested the *shissel*. I went over to her place and she went to the closet. She proudly unwrapped that old friend, because she had carefully put it away, covered with newspapers. She gave it to me. It was now my ward.

Now it came to my home - and joined my little family. But; the day I wanted to mix the soil it rained and I kept the *shissel* in the kitchen.

"I'm gonna use it to mix soil when I plant the tomatoes," I explained to my wife.

"Yich!" she commented. "How ugly. Couldn't you get one of those pretty pink plastic containers they sell in the hardware store?"

If *shissels* could cry - that one would have cried. It wasn't just a plain *shissel* - it had character. It was part of the family. It was with us in happy moments and always served us well in all emergencies. True, it was not a really pretty pan - but then again how pretty could a pan be?

"Don't worry. I'll put it out in the garage if it bothers you," I replied.

And that night, just before we went to sleep, my son accidentally bumped into the huge dieffenbachia plant we have growing in a pot in the living room and knocked it over. The flower pot smashed into a hundred pieces. The plant was an extremely valuable one for a number of reasons. First of all, it was an anniversary gift from my children on our last anniversary and besides, it was extremely expensive.

It must have been about midnight when my wife began to sigh, "Oh gee, what will we do with the plant until tomorrow? If I don't put it in water or soil, the roots will dry up and it'll die." Then she paused, "Say, what did you do with that ugly *shissel* you brought from your mother's this afternoon?"

"I put it in the garage!" I explained.

"Get it quick, we might be able to save the plant after all!" she said quickly.

So I ran out into the garage, found the *shissel*, that must have been crying all the while, and brought it back into the house. We scooped up the soil and I added some more soil I had prepared for the tomato plants and we gently placed the huge dieffenbachia plant in the middle. How proud that little *shissel* must have been. The dieffenbachia was almost like royalty.

We placed it in the living room as the leaves on the plant began to droop. "Gee, I hope the shock of the broken pot doesn't kill that plant," she said sadly.

"Don't worry – that old *shissel* will bring it back. It comforted us when we had sprained ankles, and shared happy moments with us. It served us well all these years. I knew Mama saved it for a reason."

My wife nodded like I was a nut – after all, how much character could a *shissel* have?

And so the following morning when we awoke the dieffenbachia was just about back to normal. Her leaves were proud and her color beautiful. I could almost see that little *shissel* smile.

"Wanna buy that new flower pot today?" I asked my wife as she sat studying the plant in the *shissel*.

"Not really – you know that *shissel* is beginning to grow on me. Let's leave the plant in it for a while – I think the two of them need each other."

And you know something – that *shissel* almost glowed. The tired grey porcelain basin with its many little chipped places almost looked perfect. And the plant had never thrived so well in its life.

I told a gardener friend about the plant and the shissel and he said, "Can't be anything else except that the roots now have a chance to spread out, they feel free and will give a fuller foliage."

So he says! – But I prefer to believe – that little *shissel* was created to serve humanity!

THE APARTMENT GETS PAINTED

When we were kids we looked forward with excitement and anticipation to all that went with 'ah painting' of the apartment.

HENEVER WE HAD A PAINTING MAMA WOULD start complaining weeks before. Nevertheless we looked forward to the gypsy-like mess that followed with everything thrown all over the place. Listen, that came with 'ah painting.'

There was another reason we loved 'ah painting.' That reason was Hymie Seligman. Hymie was the painter our landlord always hired to paint his apartments. Let me tell you something, when Hymie Seligman painted an apartment – he could have charged admission. Hymie was not only a craftsman but a performer. When Hymie was working on an apartment, all the neighbors on the floor would bring chairs and sit in the hallway just to watch him paint and hear him deliver a lecture on any subject, from raising children to solving the economic problems of the nation. Hymie's words were quoted and requoted by the women in our building - even weeks after a painting. "Pearls fell from his mouth," Mrs. Mermelstein, Mama's old neighbor used to say, "Real pearls fell from the mouth."

To tell the truth, I don't think anybody really knew what Hymie was talking about. But, he spoke with such great conviction you had to swear he was right. When I mentioned old Hymie Seligman to Mama, she beamed, "You *takeh* remember Seligman - dot wuz a painter!" If Hymie was only doing a kitchen and a bathroom - he gave short lectures. But when he worked on a living room, he gave a dissertation!"

All I could honestly remember was that Hymie had an opinion for everything from athlete's foot to how to rid the world of the dreaded African tse tse fly. When Hymie spoke his eyes would twinkle. His painter's hat was always cocked to the back of his head like an airplane pilot. He would punctuate each word with a staccato brush movement that was really something to see. A verbal ballet!

I'll never forget the first time Hymie came to paint our apartment. For weeks, Mama was telling my little brother Berel that if he wasn't a good boy the painter wouldn't come. Berel didn't have any idea what Mama was talking about. But since she said the painter wouldn't come if he was bad - Berel figured the painter had to mean something good! Sure enough the fateful morning arrived. Promptly at seven-thirty A.M. the doorbell rang. Still in his underwear - my little brother Berel ran to the door with great anticipation. G-d only knew what he was to expect.

"Who's there?" Berel called out.

"Hymie, the painter!" the voice responded.

Berel opened the door and there stood Hymie - with his white coveralls stiff with the sprinkling of paint from hundreds of jobs he had done before. His paint-splattered ladder rested against the wall. Cans of paint were at his feet and a broad smile was on his face. "Fine?" he questioned. "Go get your mother, Sonny."

Mama came to the door and greeted Hymie like a long lost cousin. "Seligman - I'm so glad Schwartz sent you. You know he used another man for Rubenstein's apartment last month and *oy, vus far ah shlumper* - he got paint all over the windows. Come in, come in."

Hymie was like one of the family! He picked up his cans of paint, headed straight for the bathroom and placed all the cans in the bathtub. He went back for his ladder, drop cloths and brushes and piled everything in the bathtub.

"Come, you'll have a glass of tea before you start," Mama suggested hospitably.

We watched from the other room and were really impressed that Mama would extend such courtesies to a person who wasn't even a relative. We thought - oh, how important this man must be!

Actually Mama was buttering up Hymie. She wanted a rose color in the living room and the landlord said it would take two coats to cover the blue that was on the walls. So, with a *glezeleh* tea and a piece of honey cake, Mama felt she could get Hymie to give her the rose color. Hymie would agree with Mama, that the old color blue looked horrible and said he would be more than happy to make the room rose - but of course, it would cost Mama fifteen dollars - "After all," Hymie would drawl, "paint costs money, and dot takes two coats!"

Hymie would finish his tea, then go back to the bathroom where he brought out a huge can of paint. He marched back to the kitchen, turned to Mama and asked, "What color you want in the kitchen - yellow, eggshell, or canary yellow?"

"Whatsmatter with plain white?" Mama would question.

Plain white will cost you extra - Schwartz only pays me

to put on yellow. *Nu?*"

Mama thought for a moment and said, "All right, make it canary yellow."

Hymie promptly opened the can of paint and began to paint. "You're lucky, that's just the color I brought up!"

The truth was – it was the only color he had. Our landlord, Schwartz, used to pick up bargains in the paint stores and whenever he came across a store that had some white paint that was already turning yellow – he got it for a fraction of the price. This, Schwartz told the tenants, was canary yellow – "like from ah young canary!"

After, Hymie would begin painting. Mama would question, "Listen, Finkelstein next door had her kitchen done in canary yellow and it's a different color. How come?"

Hymie would continue painting and casually reply, "In a few weeks this color will be like hers. Paint has to age on the wall." What he meant was that the paint would keep turning yellow because of its age. If Mama seemed unhappy, Hymie would cheer her up with – "Listen, get me a few jars – I'll spill off a little paint so you'll have paint to touch up, in case the children smear the wall." Gee! How magnanimous, we thought! How were we to know whatever paint he had left over he had to throw out anyway! The clincher was if he threw in a little clean turpentine to take off any of the splattered paint from the floor, it was always worth an extra five dollars! I want you to know we had little jars of dried up paint in our hall closet for years. We never really used these little touch-up jars – but it was nice to know we had them.

If Mama would also give Hymie lunch – as a gesture of good will he would paint the toilet seat with the same color enamel paint he would use on the window. This naturally would take about a week to dry! During this period we made loads of new friends in the building!

Hymie had a reputation for being the only painter in the neighborhood who could match any color you wanted, perfectly. Mama, for example, wanted the living room a certain shade of rose. She cut a piece of paper from a magazine with the color. This she gave Hymie. In less than five minutes he had the color mixed so perfectly that even the biggest maven in the building - Mrs. Mermelstein - could not tell the difference between the sample and the paint.

Actually, Hymie was a terrible color mixer. What he did was mix up a shade that was fairly close to the color Mama wanted. Then he'd paint over the piece of paper. Naturally when Mama came in and looked at the paint on the walls and the piece of paper to compare the shade - it matched perfectly!

Shoen! But that was Hymie's secret.

THE SCHOOL NOTEBOOK

Nu, so the moment of truth had arrived. There was going to be a notebook inspection in school, and if Berel didn't pass the inspection - no promotion!

I AM REALLY CONVINCED, THE MORE THINGS change, the more they remain the same! Here, let me give you 'ah f'rinstance'.

When we were kids we knew only two kinds of books: one was the Bible and the other our school notebook. And if you had a shlumpy kid brother around the house - already - you got the picture! My little brother kept a notebook like it was a disaster report culled from ancient ruins. That notebook looked like it was dipped in chicken soup twice a day and rubbed with garlic at least once a week.

I swear, it was probably the first garbage disposal unit

known to mankind! Whenever the teachers would give the little monster a notice to take home, he would diligently put it in the notebook. If and when those notices ever arrived home, it was a family effort to paste them together to see what the teacher wanted. Ninety percent of the notices, somehow or other, between the school and the house, were devoured by that notebook.

No matter what came out of that notebook, everything had a deckled edge!

At the beginning of the year Mama would run downstairs to the candy store and buy us all new notebooks - you know the kind with those little Rorshach designs on the cover. When she would bring the books upstairs and distribute them to the tribe, my little brother Berel would take his book, sit down at the dining room table and like one of the great masters write his name on the cover. He would write so neatly, you could *plotz!* We would all admire his scrawl and take a good look at the book because that would be the last time it ever looked so neat - of course - there was nothing in it!

I want you to know, that if it rained, and the sun came out, and if there was one puddle left on the block - Berel would manage to find it, trip in front of it and make certain the book landed in the middle! In less than a week, that book looked like it had gone through the flood with Noah!

Toward the end of the term the teacher would remind the children that their notebooks would be inspected. She would say, "And remember, tomorrow will be notebook inspection. Anyone who doesn't have a neat notebook will not be promoted!"

This was the moment of truth! The monster would come home, run into the bathroom and begin lathering up his notebook cover to wash away the million ink smears. My sisters would give him a soap eraser to see if he could clean up some of the pages where he doodled pictures of Dick Tracy - but it made things worse!

On another page was a series of tic-tac-toe games that

Berel had apparently played with one of his classmates during an arithmetic lesson. As a matter of fact Berel was quite good - he won six out of ten games! But he got every math example wrong.

On every page there was some *chazzerei*. Ketchup smears adorned every other page in a lovely polka dot fantasy that blended gracefully with the chicken schmaltz stains. In the binding of another page were a few pieces of *gribiness* he had left over from one lunch. I'll tell you this - that book smelled like a garbage can that had been left in the sun!

First of all Mama was no academician - but even she realized that Berel's notebook would not win any awards in scholarship! "Come *tateleh*," she exclaimed as the little monster started to cry, realizing the errors of his way. "Come, we'll go to the candy store and buy a nice new notebook you can show the teacher! Will she be proud of your nice clean pages! We'll copy over the book. How many pages could the teacher give?"

Mama got the notebook and right away Berel began to rewrite. He started out by spending an hour writing his name neatly on the front cover. "See, Ma - how neat I am!" he shouted into the kitchen while Mama was making supper.

"Look, dummy," I shouted, "forget the name on the cover, start copying over your homeworks and for crying out tears don't eat a chicken schmaltz sandwich while doing it!"

"Ma-a-a-a-a," he screamed, "see he's starting up again!"

"*Schreib, tateleh*," Mama called back. "Write nicely!"

Berel turned to the first page of the book and began recopying the notes the teacher put on the board the very first day of the term which told the kids what school supplies they had to purchase.

"Look stupid," I shouted, "You don't have to recopy that - she'll know this isn't the same book you started with! Start recopying the homework examples on the next page!"

"Ma-a-a-a-a," he screamed once more, "The teacher will kill me if I don't have all the notes!"

"Do what you want!" I snapped and walked out of the room. My older sister came in as the first relief nudgerer!

"Start writing dope!" she began softly.

"Ma-a-a-a," he screamed again. "See, she's starting up also!"

He started to copy the first page of spelling words over where he had drawn a picture of Batman! Then he stopped.

"What's the matter?" my sister questioned.

"I almost forgot I didn't have to write these words down when she gave them to us – she said we had to memorize them! So I'm skipping them."

"Skip!" she snapped. "Go on to the next page!"

He turned to the next page and there were a few homework examples that looked like they were written by a pigeon that had walked across the page with ink on its claws. At the top of the page, in red crayon, were the words, "Do Over."

"Did you do them over?" my sister asked the little dope.

"Yeah," he muttered, "but I lost the page!"

"So do them over now!" she added.

"But I'll have to copy the page I did wrong. She'll know it isn't the real notebook."

"Dummy," she shouted, "the teacher only wants to know that you know how to do the examples!"

"But she'll yell on me! She'll kill me! I'll get left back and it will be your fault!"

"So copy over the wrong examples!" my sister screamed back.

He scribbled down the examples which came out worse than the first time he had written them.

"Now I need a red pencil to write the words "Do Over!"

Nu? So *auf t'zu luches* we had only a blue crayon and a red crayon that wasn't the same shade the teacher used.

"Use the red one, she'll never know the difference," my sister coaxed.

"She'll know! She'll know! You don't know my teacher," he screamed.

Mama heard the commotion and went through the building asking all our neighbors for a red crayon pencil that matched the one in his notebook.

Then he turned to a page that was supposed to be geography. He had scrawled on that page something that looked like a cardiogram.

"What's that?" my sister asked.

"A map of New York City!" he replied.

"It looks like an amoeba giving birth with a paramecium looking on," my sister commented. The paramecium was supposed to be Staten Island!

"Ma-a-a-a-a," he whined again, "Ma, I need a map of New York to copy from."

We tore the house apart looking for a map of New York City. Listen, who had a map of New York City in the house in those days? Europe, yes. Africa, yes. But go know some idiot teacher would want a map of New York City!

I quickly ran downstairs to a gas station a few blocks away and borrowed a map from the dealer. I opened it up in front of Berel and he began copying it.

In a few minutes I walked over to see how he was doing – and almost dropped dead. The little idiot was copying down "Esso Gas."

"Dope!" I shouted, "You don't have to put that down. Just copy the map!"

He erased the Esso insignia and started drawing the map. Oy what a map! It looked like a pretzel that never quite made it. Staten Island he lost altogether.

"Make sure you write New York City under the map," I ordered, "otherwise the teacher will think you're drawing obscene pictures!"

It was now eleven o'clock at night.

"Go to sleep already!" Mama ordered.

"I didn't finish my notebook and if I don't bring it in tomorrow I'll get left back!" he cried scribbling even more feverishly.

"Don't worry, I wouldn't throw you out of the house if you get left back," Mama explained trying to quiet his tears.

"She will! She will!" he cried even more bitterly.

"Don't worry *tateleh*," Mama cooed once more, "Papa will take your teacher up to a wholesale house so she could get a new coat wholesale. She asked me already. Remember last term you were afraid the teacher would leave you back and Papa made her a nice beige suit he sold to her wholesale. Don't worry, you wouldn't get left back."

Berel finally agreed to go to bed when Mama and Papa convinced him we would finish copying over the book for him. My sisters and I took turns trying to imitate his Chinese scrawl. *Oy*, was that a chore. We couldn't figure out half of what he had in the book.

We finally got to sleep about 2 A.M. but the book was finished! And it didn't look bad!

Berel was up bright and early inspecting the notebook we had written for him. He had his breakfast, then tucked the book proudly under his arm and started out for school.

Then it happened! That afternoon he came home from school in tears!

"What happened?" we asked him.

"I lost the notebook in school!" he blurted out. "We went to gym and I put the book down someplace and it wasn't there when I got back!"

Mama turned pale but tried to comfort him.

"So take the old notebook this afternoon and show it to your teacher. I'll give you a note telling the teacher it was my fault you left the book home. Don't worry, she wouldn't leave you back!"

Mama put his old notebook near the stove to dry up from the soapy water Berel got all over it the day before he took the recopied book to school.

Came three o'clock we all got nervous stomachs, waiting for Berel to come home. Finally the bell rang and he walked in all smiles.

"I passed! I passed!" he shouted.

"How?" we all shouted. "With that notebook?"

"My teacher even wrote a note in the book to Mama," he exclaimed.

We opened the book and there was piece of paper inside the cover. It was a note from his teacher. It read:

"Mrs. Fine,

This is not what I would call the best notebook I have ever had to check. In fact, I wore gloves when I marked it. But, it is truly the most honest one turned in this term. All the other children rewrote their notebooks and although neat and exacting they left out a great deal of the work that dealt with the corrected homework. This I consider important because it is done to show children how they grow academically. Berel's book was also a chronicle of my appearance during the term. I do not eat onions! The child was in error! It is heartwarming to know there are parents who will not teach their children to cheat by rewriting notebooks. When can your husband take me up to that wholesale house for a coat?"

Nu? Like I said before – the more things change the more they remain the same!

MR. KESSELMAN
AND THE STOCK MARKET

When we were kids, next to President Roosevelt we thought Mama's third floor neighbor, Izzy Kesselman, was the most important man in the country.

R. KESSELMAN WAS A SHORT STOCKY GENTLE-man who always had a cigar stub sticking out of his mouth. Whenever he spoke he commanded attention. His opening words were always the same: "*Herh zich ein...*" (Listen to me). But they were said with such warmth - you were certain he was going to tell you a great secret.

Mr. Kesselman worked "in the stock market." We had heard Mama and Papa always talking about "Kesselman from der stock market - *err vaist allis* - everything he knows."

Actually, Mr. Kesselman was little more than a clerk in

a stock brokerage house that employed nearly a hundred people. But to hear Mr. Kesselman talk - you would swear he was the president!

When he would come into our house for a visit, Papa would smile and say, "*Nu* - Kesselman, *vus hert zich?*" (What do you hear?)

And Mr. Kesselman would look very serious and sigh soulfully, "*Ich vais? Ess is nit goot.* (You think I know? It's not so good.) The market is slipping."

Neither Mama nor Papa knew anything about the stock market. And since Kesselman was on Wall Street and since we were told, "How goes Wall street, so goes the nation," this was serious talk. Mr. Kesselman would bite on his cigar and say, "*Her zich ein* (listen to me) - I was talking to Rosenstein -*du vaist* Rosenstein? (you know Rosenstein?) - he's the president of my company - and Rosenstein said to me - like this he says to me - 'Kesselman, what do you think of Graber Garments Inc.?"

Mama began to prepare a glass of tea and Papa sat down with anticipation. After all, Rosenstein was a name we heard quite often. He was the president of the brokerage company that did a business in millions. In fact, that was the closest we ever got to a millionaire. Just talking about Rosenstein made us feel wealthy.

"*Nu?*" Papa asked in hushed tones, "*Vus hut ehr du gezukt?* (What did he say to you?) After all, if Rosenstein asks you a question, you must answer...no?"

"*Avada*, of course! When Rosenstein asks - *nu* - you answer! Listen - he's the boss." Kesselman spoke with such sincerity you were certain he had the inside track on everything.

"*Nu*, so Rosenstein asks and I said, 'To me Graber Garments Inc. is *nisht ahere and nisht ahin.* (Not here nor there.) Why do you ask?' " Kesselman sighed and sipped his tea. "Like dot - I said to him - just like dot. I'm not afraid to answer."

"So what did Rosenstein ask about Graber Garments

for?" Papa asked.

"Why?" Kesselman began rhetorically. "Because Graber wants an underwriting! He needs money to buy out a special run of material Forstman goods is making up."

Papa had been in the garment center almost all of his life and the very mention of Forstman goods meant quality merchandise.

"So what happened?" Papa pressed him.

"So I told Rosenstein, if Graber uses Forstman he must be making quality merchandise. I told him it's worth the risk," Kesselman explained. "So from what I se't, Graber will get the money. Just like dot!" Kesselman felt so proud. "Why shouldn't we help our own?" Mama was so impressed and Papa couldn't get over how important Kesselman was that the boss of a million dollar concern should come to him for advice.

"Listen," Kesselman went on, "I'll put you in on the ground floor when they have the underwriting. After all, if we can't take care of our own – who else should we take care of? After all, who are you? *Ah Fremdeh mench*? (A stranger?) You're a neighbor! Dot's why I'm telling you the inside dope. After all, a man like Rosenstein – *er vais fun allis!*" (He knows everything!)

Our finances during those early years were a little less than what we needed. And the last people Kesselman could have asked to go into the market were Mama and Papa. But whose business was it? Kesselman's? We always appeared wealthy.

Papa thought for a moment and said, "I'd go in – but we just bought some stock and we're a little short right now – but the minute I have a little extra – you'll hear."

Kesselman stood up, shrugged his shoulders, dumping cigar ashes over his vest and said, "Listen – I'm doing this because you're a friend. To me it's not'ten – to me absolutely not'ten! *Nu* – so when you'll want, you'll ask."

When Kesselman left, that's when it first started. Mama got on the phone and called a cousin. The conversation usually went like this. "Hello, Chaya? *Vus hert zich*? (What do you hear?) How's everybody?"

And cousin Chaya would reply, "*Denks gut*, everybody is getting over with colds and *denks gut – vus hert zich*?" (Thank G-d – what do you hear?)

Mama would talk softly – "Listen Chaya, Kesselman, you know Kesselman my neighbor – from Wall Street? He just gave us ah tip!"

Cousin Chaya would say – "*Nu, nu – vus hut er gezukt*? (So, so – what did he say?) What he se't?"

Mama would whisper – Graber Garments Inc. They make coats with Forstman's goods. *Du vaist foon* Forstman's? (You know Forstman) D'ots one hundret pu'cent merchandise."

"Aha," cousin Chaya would gasp – "Nu, *vifil cost ess*? How much it's selling for?"

Mama replied, "*Ich vais nit*, (I don't know.) only Kesselman said we should buy – his company is writing it under!"

"Aha," cousin Chaya would echo – I'll call Sophie – she has ah son a lawyer – he'll know! Denks for the tip. By the way – you going to Sadie's daughter's wedding? I wouldn't go – because me they'll sit with the Merbaums. You know, from Toledo – them I don't talk to."

And so it went. Cousin Chaya called Sophie's son who was a lawyer. He always talked her out of making a purchase, and into making a purchase of something he was involved in. Inevitably his stock would drop like a rock when Chaya bought. I should point out, Graber Garments went on the market at one price and stayed at one price for years – until Graber went bankrupt!

One day Mama was shopping in the fish store and Mrs. Kesselman leaned over to Mama and whispered, "Listen, Izzy came home last night and bought a t'ousand shares from Electric Telegraph and Telephone Ohio – dot's a new stock what is going to really move!" Mama listened intently.

Mrs. Kesselman continued, "But Izzy isn't telling

nobody because he's afraid it'll go too high and there'll be an investigation! But, you I'm telling because you're a friend and a neighbor. After all, if we can't help our own who should we help?" She had the same script writer as Izzy.

Mama was so tantalized that she went upstairs and dug into her little *knipple* (her rainy day money). She pulled out a few dollars and called another cousin, an accountant, to make the purchase of the stock.

"What's the name? cousin David asked.

"I think she said something like a telephone and a telegraph set – *ich vais nit* (I don't know) – I forgot to write it down."

"You probably mean International Tel and Tel – I know what you want..." Cousin David explained and he went out and made the purchase. But it had to be hush-hush. Papa shouldn't know! David was on Mama's side of the family so the secret was secure.

Sure enough, the days turned into months, and the months into years. Then the Wall Street crash came. Mrs. Kesselman came down to Mama in tears. Their life savings had been wiped out.

"But what happened?" Mama asked as Mrs. Kesselman sobbed. "The stock you told me to get is very nice, I still keep getting checks from them every few months," Mama confided.

"Oompossible!" Mrs. Kesselman sobbed, "they were wiped out! They went bankrupt six months after I told you three years ago!"

"What you talking?" Mama snapped. "Here I'll show you!" And she took out some check stubs and coupons from the company.

"You bought the wrong one!" Mrs. Kesselman screamed. "You didn't buy w'ot I told you. Dot's the wrong one!"

Mama shrugged – and breathed a sigh of relief. A little later Mr. Kesselman stopped in. He was tired and drawn. He drew such compassion from you. Everything they had ever saved was invested in Kesselman's inside tips. And his "tips" went down the drain.

He sat down at the table for a glass of tea and sighed. Just then the phone rang. It was cousin Chaya. "Listen," she said, "I just got a tip from my butcher – he told me ah company what makes adding machines is going to be very big. It must be a Jewish concern because they only use their initials. It's called I.B.M."

Mama thanked cousin Chaya and then told the Kesselmans. Mr. Kesselman leaned back and chewed on his cigar. He was the stock maiven – he should know.

"I.B.M." he mused, "wot kind of name is dot?" he questioned. "Wot do they make?"

"Adding machines! Chaya says it must be a Jewish concern because they use only initials – it's probably something like Itzkowitz, Bernstein and Moscowitz – but they figure for business purposes it's better to use initials."

"They make adding machines?" echoed Kesselman. "Wot kind of business is that? For a dope you need an adding machine! A smart person uses a pencil and a paper! And who can't add! For children yes – but for business – *feh* – stay away! Dot's not for you...stay away..."

THE STREETS OF GOLD

When papa was a boy in the old country he had heard, "In America the streets are paved with gold!" Not only did he discover they weren't paved with gold – he was lucky to find a street that was paved!

WHEN PAPA ARRIVED IN AMERICA HE DISCOVered that the gold that was supposed to grow on trees had already been picked by others. Papa soon found that he had to work nearly around the clock in a garment center sweat shop to barely make a living.

What joys did Mama and Papa have in those years? Night clubs? Movies? Maybe television? Television wasn't even used in the Buck Rogers comic strips. Radio? Only the wealthy had radios!

So what did they do for enjoyment? The old timers

made their own enjoyment. They formed "Benevolent and Fraternal Societies" each with the name of the community from which they came.

Nu, so I asked Papa - "What kind of enjoyment could you have gotten from going to a meeting every week? What did you discuss?"

"What?" Papa challenged, "We would argue over who would be the next president of the organization... "

"When would this argument begin?"

"The day after the new president was sworn in - so we had a whole year's worth of discussion," Papa explained.

"So a whole meeting was taken up with this?" I questioned.

"Of course not," Papa began. "We would also argue about where we should buy cemetery plots for the members. Some wanted Jersey and some wanted Long Island so it should be near their family."

"Was this such a big deal?" I questioned.

"Big?" Papa gasped. He explained that this was the whole purpose of the society. After all, these people were in a new country. Who did they know? In Europe, when someone passed away, the community always took care. But in America? Who? So they would argue about which cemetery we would buy from.

"Nu, so what else did you discuss at the meeting besides who the next president of the society would be and the cemetery plots?" I queried.

"What else was there to argue about?" he concluded.

This discussion brought back a wonderful memory.

I'll never forget the time Papa's society held an open meeting - that meant the wives and children could attend. I remember it was in the middle of the winter. Mama dressed us up in our long underwear and we made the trek to the subway to take the train to the Forward building on the Lower East Side of New York.

When we entered the building we got on an elevator that let us off on a floor that just reeked of pickled herring and onions. Oy – hut es geshmeckt! Did it smell delicious!

Papa and Mama were greeted by our uncles and aunts and we greeted our cousins who were already knee deep in pickled herring.

Then the meeting started. The president knocked with a gavel and announced in Yiddish that the meeting was to start. The secretary read the minutes of the previous meeting that everyone immediately accepted – because no one listened.

Then the president began – "*Brieder und shvester* (Brothers and sisters) – this is indeed a happy occasion for us because last week we closed a deal with the New Jersey cemetery and I'm happy to announce that right after we signed, our brother, Hyman Cohen passed away and he was the first to use the premises. It was a lovely location covered with trees. However, the cemetery officials said they would take away the trees if any brother or sister didn't want to lie in the shade!"

Everyone applauded. After all, this was an "extra" they would not be charged for.

"And now for more happy news," he continued. "I'm pleased to announce that our Sunshine Committee is functioning perfectly because last month the committee visited nineteen brothers and sisters who were deathly ill, and I am pleased to report six have recovered. If the others don't recover we know it will be a comfort for them to know we got the plot they wanted at the price we wanted."

He took a deep breath and continued. "I also want you to know that we were very lucky because one of the members who we thought was going to pass away last week did not. He passed away yesterday, and it was a very successful funeral. We will all rise for a moment of silence for our dear departed brother and give the caterer a chance to put out the coffee and cake. Please, children, away from the door."

We all stood up and *takeh* the "caterer," a greasy looking character, put out a dish with sponge cake and a big container of coffee.

"After the collation we will go on with the meeting," the president announced. "We have much good news for this open meeting. It is indeed a pleasure to see all the *vibelach* (women) and the *kinder* (children) and everybody, the *ganza mishpocha* (the whole family) enjoying the herring dot was donated to us by brother Levy, wot's got an appetizing store on Jennings Street. Please stop in and give him a break."

By the time we turned around the sponge cake was gone. When Mama asked the president how come they didn't have more sponge cake, the president said, "We bought so much - I can't believe it's all gone! Wait I'll ask the caterer. Chaim," he called out toward the kitchen section of the hall, "Where is the sponge cake?"

The caterer grumbled back, "Dey ate it! Wot do you mean - where iss?"

The president continued the debate, "Listen, the people want a piece of sponge cake with coffee, *gib ah kuk* (take a look) around the kitchen and see wot you can find."

Then he turned to Mama and explained, "*Vart, ut kompt* (Wait, it's coming) more sponge cake!"

Then he would dart away to a small group on the side who were arguing about how high a cemetery headstone should be. One cousin was arguing, "I heard dot the new style in America is with the little stones, you know *die kleinchikeh shtainer* (the little stones.) Dot's what dey are doing on all da moddren cemeteries."

Another cousin chimed in, "I saw wot dey got - dey look like imitation stones. It doesn't look real. Real imitation - listen we pay enough we should get the real thing - who needs imitation when you can get the best?"

My little brother Berel turned to Mama and questioned what they were talking about.

"It's not for your ears *tateleh*," Mama exclaimed, so right away Berel ran over to me and whispered, "I think they're talking dirty - Mama said I shouldn't listen!"

So right away we all ran over and tuned in. By this time

the president was knocking with the gavel once more.

"*Brieder und shvester* (brothers and sisters) let us finish the meeting. Now dot we had some of the collation -we have full stomachs and we can talk business. I also have more good news from our casket committee. They made a private negotiation with a casket manufacturer dot we can get caskets, only for the paid up members, at less than wholesale. Of course, they are last year's model, but, at the prices they quoted we couldn't pass up. *Luz mir alleh, zine shtark* (Let us all be strong) - and healthy and we shouldn't have to use one but it is nice to show on the financial statement dot we got them at our price."

He took a quick drink from a glass of water near his side and continued. "Also more happy news - we sold off sixteen plots and from the old cemetery wot we had in Long Island and bought for that money twenty-one in Jersey."

The president then announced, "And now since this is our installation meeting we will install the new officers for the coming year."

There was moderate applause, with a lot of hustling and bustling around the rostrum. Then the president announced, "And now I will install the new president." He turned and smiled, "Since I'm also the new president for the next year I install myself."

Everybody applauded. "Brother Shepsel was re-elected secretary-treasurer and the corresponding scribe will be my wife, Yitta. I wish you all congratulations for the coming year. Now, please eat something in the back or the children will eat up everything and will be sick tomorrow. Next month, we will have nominations for next year's president and his helpers. *Ess*, (eat) please *ess* the fish and the cake."

When we turned around - there was no more fish left and no more cake.

Then Papa's sister came over and said, "Come we'll go downstairs to the cafeteria - the children didn't have a thing. Everybody ate like a horse and the poor children are starved."

We got our coats and as we started to leave the president stood by the door and questioned, "So early?"

And my aunt smiled, "*Die kinder* (the children)- they have school on Monday."

"But tonight is Saturday, they could sleep a whole day Sunday," he replied almost concerned.

"Dot's right," my aunt smiled back, "but they have homework," and she quickly pushed us into the elevator.

We went down to the ground floor and then into a little cafeteria on the corner of Essex Street. Papa grabbed a table and then went to the counter. He brought back some milk for us and a tray filled with cookies and sponge cake.

Just as we sat down, sure enough, three quarters of the membership of the society filed into the cafeteria and headed for the milk and cookie section.

In less time than it takes to tell, the whole membership was in the cafeteria including the president, who stood up to make an announcement.

"Tierer brieder und shvester, (Dear brothers and sisters) I have some good new to tell you about..."

But before he could finish everyone shouted him down with, "*Yetz haben mir bazult* (here we paid our own money) so we don't have to listen!"

He was a little hurt, but sat down and began sipping his glass of tea as he looked through his brief case filled with a display of caskets in full color.

Yes, those were the days of societies and many of them still exist to this very day with the sons and sons-in-law of the founders still making them function.

THE FRIENDLY SOUNDS OF YESTERDAY

The world of yesterday may be gone but the sounds are still here, if only in our memories, as an echo bouncing off the tenement walls.

AY WHAT YOU WANT! TODAY'S WORLD IS DIF-
ferent. Yesterday's world was a world of friendly sounds.
Once upon a time the clip-clop-clip-clop of the milkman's
horse in the early hours of the morning was a kind of
comfort. You knew there was somebody else up at that hour
of the morning and if you had to scream for help - that sound
told you somebody was not too far away.

The old sound of the trolley cars that rode down the
streets on glimmering steel rails had a friendly squeal as they
rounded a corner. That was the overture, part of the
symphony of sound in the night. The sound of the trolley's

---

air brake told you it was stopping to discharge people who might be walking down your block. It was comforting to know there were people around in those still hours. During the day the clang of the trolley bell announced it's presence and set the pace of the day.

In those years many of the stores on the Lower East Side of New York were owned by families who lived "in the back." Connected to a piece of flimsy coat hanger wire near the front door was a little bell that would tinkle every time the door opened. It would alert those in the back. The bell would tinkle and in a few seconds it would be followed by the cheerful words of the owner who would come from behind a dull grey curtain that separated the store from the living quarters in the back.

In the apartment houses of old there were dumbwaiters. The dumbwaiter was a shaft that had a very small box that operated like an elevator. In the evening, the superintendent would press a button in the basement that rang a bell in your apartment. You opened the dumbwaiter door, put your can of garbage on the dumbwaiter and the garbage was hoisted down to the basement. There, the superintendent would empty the can and return it to your floor via the dumbwaiter. During the non-garbage collecting times, the dumbwaiter had many other uses. It was a unique communications system. On the cold winter days when Mama couldn't call to her neighbors through the window, she would merely open the dumbwaiter and call down to her neighbor, who would then open her dumbwaiter door and talk back. Sometimes if the conversation was lively three or four other tenants on the same dumbwaiter line would join in! It was a toll-free party line.

In the years not so long passed there were always ice men who delivered cakes of ice for the ice box. This was before the era of refrigerators. The chopping sound of the ice man chopping out a piece of ice from the huge block on his wagon was always an interesting sound. It followed a perfect staccato rhythm. When some of the ice men installed motorized ice cutters on their trucks – part of that great world of individualized sound was lost. Those little gasoline engines that were used with the cutters made a terrible racket. Yup, that had to be the beginning of noise pollution!

In every old-time neighborhood there was always a live poultry market. In those years the customers insisted on having fresh chicken and the poultry were kept alive in little wooden cages. The cackle of the chickens during the tumult of the day would soften to a hushed silence toward the evening until a stray dog would approach the chicken market window and bark. The chickens would return the bark with their tearful cackle! How sorry we felt for them.

The sounds of yesterday have been replaced with today's sounds. The hoofbeats of the milkman's horse in the early morning hours have been replaced by the sounds of cars starting and stopping in front of your house. Or maybe someone's car alarm going off to wail in the stillness of the night. Now, you run to the window to make sure someone isn't stealing your car! After all, who hears a car start in the quiet of the night or in the early morning hours – especially if it is in front of our house. What's the first thought? Right! Someone is trying to steal the car or at least take the radio.

The only sound that remains the same today is that of the subway trains. I remember years ago when you could hear those elevated trains for blocks and how we felt sorry for the people who lived near the Simpson Street station of the IRT which was almost ten feet away from the tracks. How we would try to look into their apartments as we rode by. Oh, how that noise drove them crazy, we thought. But then we made friends with a family who had such an apartment and when we went there for dinner, after the first hour you couldn't hear the trains anymore, we grew so used to it.

Today, the symphony of New York has changed. The instrumentation is different. The jet aircraft that wander overhead in the stillness of the night sound so angry. The occasional propeller driven plane now sounds like a hum.

When jet airliners first appeared on the scene, oy, how everybody complained about their noise! See, we didn't know when we were well off!

Today, the overture is gone. If you buy a car, the first thing they do is lock you inside to show you how soundproof it is. Big deal! Who wants it soundproof? They sell you a soundproof car then they try to talk you into installing an FM radio with twelve stereo speakers. Vere daf dos? (Who needs this?)

On Friday afternoons in our old house, as you walked through the halls you heard the chop-chop-chop of the many women preparing the gefilte fish. The fish was chopped in a wooden bowl and it too had a rhythm and melody of its own. Each chopper had her own original orchestration.

During the day, you heard the milk bottles being placed in the hallway for the milkman to pick up. You heard the thump of the wooden seltzer crates the seltzer man would shlep up three flights of stairs as he came to deliver the Friday order for seltzer. Seltzer at a Friday night table was almost a ritual.

After supper there was always the same sound of dishes being washed, water running, the tinkle of spoons and glasses against the stone of the sink. Today that sound is all but gone - replaced by the whir of washing machines. The old vash breitel (washing board) on which Mama must have washed thousands of pieces of clothing in those years was retired years ago along with its own deep basso pizzicato sound. Now, there are no more sounds - the plastic laundry baskets don't make a sound as the laundry is taken to the basement washing machines.

Today's world of sounds is different. You walk through the halls of an apartment house and you hear either a confusion of sounds with everybody turned to different TV stations - or you hear the wildest stereo with the same station coming from a hundred different doors.

I'll never forget one neighbor who told us her brother

had a special job in Detroit at one of the automobile plants. All he did was listen to the motors of the new cars that rolled off the assembly lines – and just by listening he would diagnose what was wrong with each car. Oh how we marveled at such a person. "He just listens a whole day long," she would exclaim.

Then one Passover he came in with his family and we met him. He was a nice fellow but couldn't hear a thing people were saying to him. Listen, who am I to judge. Maybe cars he could listen to, but people – after all, who knows?

Another sound that is gone is the sound of the coal trucks that used to deliver the millions of tons of coal to heat the tenements of our city. We watched as the coal chutes were lowered from the huge grimey black truck and the coal flowed into a coal hopper with a "shhhhhhhh" sound. Then each night before we went to sleep we could hear our superintendent shovel coal into the furnace to bank it for the night. And in the morning when the steam started coming up there was the familiar clack–clunk–clink of the steam rising in the radiator pipe greeting the cold air that gathered in the pipes during the freezing night. They played a duet all their own. No two rhythms were the same! It was a familiar tempo but each morning the steam pipe melody always seemed different.

At nights, as the house grew quiet you could always hear the family upstairs when someone walked across the floor. We always knew when there was something wrong. If we heard walking sounds in the middle of the night – we knew the baby was sick and someone was preparing something to ease the pain.

Every sound had a meaning – every sound was a friend. Today this is all different. If you hear footsteps in the streets at night – you get a funny feeling that maybe it's a mugger or a thief looking for an open window. If the footsteps stop in front of your house – you hold your breath. You listen! You hear a dog bark – then another joins in, you can almost tell when they smell danger.

You can always tell when a neighbor falls asleep in front of a television set in the summer - it runs all night long and you hear the continuous beep of a test pattern that stays on through the night or maybe a movie that had come out some thirty or forty years before in plain black and white!

Indeed! The sounds of yesterday are gone forever.

THE WINTER VACATION

I'll never forget the time our teacher handed out homework for every day of the winter vacation so we wouldn't forget what we had already learned. But we got even - we forgot anyway!

THE MOST DISTRESSING THING ABOUT TODAY'S younger generation is that we don't belong to it! You have to remember, our generation was a generation of worriers. We worried about everything, especially my little brother Berel. That dopey kid would rather worry what his teacher would do to him for not doing his homework than actually do the homework.

I'll never forget how he looked forward to the winter vacation. For weeks before the holiday that kid laid out a set of plans - like he was getting ready to invade the planet Mars. He had something going for him every day.

So the last day of school before the winter vacation, his teacher decided to give her kids homework over the holiday so that the little monsters in his fifth grade class shouldn't forget what they learned the first half of the term.

His teacher had the right idea. She figured if she gave the kids a few words to write or a few examples to complete during the ten day vacation, the kids wouldn't be inconvenienced and they wouldn't forget their schoolwork.

His teacher gave them some examples for arithmetic, and a composition that required the student go to the library and look up a specific topic of his own choosing. Listen – what was so *geferlach* (terrible)?

As the kids prepared to leave on that last day of school my little brother Berel's teacher announced, "I gave you approximately five examples for each day of the vacation. The examples shouldn't take you more than a few minutes each day and by the end of the vacation you will be ready for the new work we will start."

Listen – it sounded so plausible – after all, normally Berel's teacher would give him about ten to fifteen examples every day – so just 'five a day' that was takeh (really) a vacation!

"And the composition you will research in the library during the vacation time, should be simple and complete," his teacher explained. "Make sure you write neatly."

All the little dummies in his class shook their heads – and of course none of them, least of all Berel, knew what the heck she was talking about! But why argue – it was vacation time!

So the bell rang and the little monsters ran from the school like it was on fire!

What can I tell you? The first day of vacation time arrived. Papa's boss had given him some passes to a children's program in downtown New York, so Mama bundled up the whole tribe and we went to New York to see the children's show. This we could have lived without – but listen – who looks a gift horse in the mouth?

By the time we got home we were so exhausted because Mama also stopped off at a department store for a little shopping.

So the first day was shot. By the time we got home Berel was too exhausted to do any work. He figured he would knock off ten examples the next day.

Sure enough bright and early the next morning Berel's little friend called for him and the two disappeared for the entire day playing in the street. By the time he came up he was too exhausted to do anything. *Nu* – so he figured he'd knock off fifteen examples the next day. After all, they were simple examples – what was the big hurry?

And so the next day came and the next day and the next and before we knew what was happening the whole ten day winter vacation was over.

Then that last Sunday – around ten o'clock at night Berel walked into the kitchen with tears streaming down his face muttering, "I forgot to do my homework and my teacher will kill me!"

"WHAT HOMEWORK!" Mama screamed.

"She gave us some examples and something I was supposed to write about from the library," Berel tearfully explained.

"Watsamatter a whole week you didn't have time?" Mama screamed once more. "Not one day did you pick up a book! Do you still remember how to read?"

That was a *gridger* (a dig) – adding insult to injury.

"Get your homework," Papa said.

Berel went to get his homework book and Papa tried to calm Mama down. "Listen, how much homework could it be – after all, he's only a child."

In a second Berel was back with his homework book that looked like it had been shellshocked in battle! "I got these fifty examples," he began.

"Take out a pencil and you'll do it now!" Mama announced firmly.

Berel quickly took out a stub of a pencil and began to

scribble down the first example. Then he stopped and began to cry.

"What now?" we asked him.

"I don't know what the top number is. I can't read my writing!" he tearfully exclaimed.

"Then do the next example," Mama declared sharply.

He started to scribble down a few numbers then stopped once more. "I can't read the bottom numbers. Irving Wallerman threw a snowball at me on the way home and the ink smeared!"

"Then do the next one," Mama declared even more exasperated.

He started to transcribe the next example then stopped once more. "I forgot how to do this one."

Mama gave one geshrei (shout) – "NOW YOU'LL FLUNK!"

Oy, did that phrase carry humiliation! After all, who in our family ever 'flunked' anything?

"I forgot...!" he continued to whine.

"Leave the examples," Mama shouted, "Papa and I will do the examples. Now go to sleep. *Du fakurtz meir der yoren!*" (You are shortening my years).

"I also have to do the composition about the library!" the little dope whined once more.

"What composition?" Mama shrieked. "You mean you got more homework? *Gevald!*" (My goodness!)

He took out his notebook and showed the assignment to me. It looked like it was written in a combination of ancient hieroglyphics and cuneiform. After I translated his scrawl I exclaimed, "Dummy! You were supposed to go to the library and look up a subject and write a composition about that subject on what you read in the library book!"

Mama put her hand to her head as if it were ready to fall off. "*Gevald fah der yoren!* Did you pick a subject?"

Berel looked down as if his whole world had crumpled. "I was going to write about the African tsetse fly. I had a picture of one!"

"The WHAT?" Mama screamed. "Ah tzitzis fly? What is this?"

I explained to Mama about the fly and suggested that we might be able to get some information about the subject from our encyclopedia. I ran to the bookshelf, took down the volume and began to cull the pages. Sure enough there was a whole section on the fly.

"GO TO SLEEP!" Mama shouted at him. "Your brother will write the composition. Go to sleep! Get away from my eyes. A whole week he doesn't pick up a book! A whole week!"

Berel made a beeline for the bedroom. Mama and Papa sat down with his assignment book and tried to decipher his arithmetic examples while I began to write about the African tsetse fly. Mama then turned to me and said, "Don't write with big words – the teacher will know he didn't write it."

"Ma," I exclaimed, "The teacher will know he didn't write it because it won't be in his handwriting!"

"Nu, so tomorrow morning he'll copy it over," Mama said slowly. Then from the bedroom Berel called out, "Don't make it too long!"

"Shut up and go to sleep, dope," I shouted back.

"Ma-a-a-a," he shouted from the bedroom, "see how he starts up!"

"Go to sleep," we all shouted and then set about doing Berel's homework.

Mama and Papa were able to figure out about half of the fifty examples while I put down a few pertinent facts in as simple language as possible about the African tsetse fly. We all went to bed after two in the morning.

The following morning Berel got up all bright-eyed and bushy-tailed and ran into the living room to see if the homework we did the night before met with his approval.

"Get dressed," Mama ordered, "then you'll recopy."

He got dressed and started to recopy the composition but if you knew how fast Berel wrote, you could *plotz*.

"Forget it dummy, take the one I wrote and turn it in.

Maybe the teacher won't remember your handwriting," I exclaimed in disgust.

He quickly packed his books and sailed out of the house. That afternoon when he returned from school he was all smiles.

"What happened?" I asked.

"Nothing," he exclaimed, "My old teacher isn't coming back and the new teacher we have collected all the papers and then read the best ones. She read mine, gave me an A and now she likes me."

Nu - so the A stood and that first impression his new teacher got miraculously had stayed throughout the term.

A CHRISTMAS TREE IN THE SHUL

So how does a Christmas tree come to a shul, you might ask?
A good question!

IN OUR OLD NEIGHBORHOOD, WE DIDN'T know what a Christmas tree looked like. *Chas V'sholem* – (heaven forbid) – where would we see one? Of course there were many non-Jewish people who lived in the neighborhood – but how many of them could afford a tree? We were told their kids hung their stockings up on the kitchen stove. After all, that was the only thing that even remotely resembled a chimney. But trees? *Ah nechtiger tug*! (Forget it!) Of course, some of the candy stores who sold tree decorations put little trees in their windows, gaily decorated – sort of a forshpice, a sample of what wares they sold. But that was the extent of it.

So need I tell you the commotion that took place when, of all places, a Christmas tree appeared in the window of our rabbi's study in our shul?

So let me explain. Our shul employed an old Irish gentleman who lived in the neighborhood. He worked as the superintendent of the shul. If a light burned out, John would repair it. He put coal on the fire, he cleaned the shul and the classrooms – he was in charge of the shul's maintenance.

About a week before the holidays, John left early one night to purchase a little Christmas tree for his family on the corner of Tremont Avenue and Southern Boulevard where vendors sold their holiday trees. As he was passing the shul on his way home, the rabbi called to him and told him the boiler wasn't giving off enough heat. John came into the rabbi's study, put the tree down right near the window and ran down to the boiler room. Sure enough, a valve had broken and unless it was replaced immediately there would be no heat in the shul.

John quickly ran out to a hardware store to see if he could get a new part, but they told him it was a special type of valve and the only place it could be obtained was downtown in a heating supply house. So without a moment's hesitation, he took the subway downtown to purchase the part.

Meanwhile, the shul was getting extremely cold so the rabbi locked up his office and went home. The rabbi had Yahrzeit that day and had lit two Yahrzeit glasses, placing them on a mantle in his study. With all the lights out – and John's tree in the window – it looked like the tree was lit up. The ceiling paint in that old building always flaked. Now, since the building started to get cold, that old paint just above the tree started to peel and flake down onto the branches of the tree. It gave it a beautiful snowy effect. The orange glow from the fire alarm box on the corner added the final touch. The orange light reflected off the branches like part of a decoration. Shoen! A glowing, decorated Christmas tree in the rabbi's study!

So what happened? Sure enough, the first person who happened to pass by had to be Mrs. Rabinowitz. She and her husband owned the store on 180th Street where they sold talaisim (prayer shawls) and prayer books. Do I have to go on? Mrs. Rabinowitz froze in her tracks. She stared at the tree shining in the darkness and looked up to the sky as if awaiting some word from the L-rd or at least a bolt of lightning. She quickly gathered her thoughts and ran to the corner grocery store to Mr. Perlman.

"Perlman," she gasped, "*kuk vus der Rebbe hut in der shul!*" (look what the rabbi has in the synagogue) she shouted. "Look, look -its ah Christmas tree! *Ess is der emmis!* (It's the truth) A Christmas tree! Unzerer Rebbe -*un ah Christmas tree - Chas V'Shalom!*" (Our rabbi and a Christmas tree - oh, my goodness).

Let me tell you something - if they announced that the Messiah arrived no greater turmoil could have been generated. At first Mr. Perlman made light of it. He thought Mrs. Rabinowitz was joking. When she fainted and everybody ran with a glass of water, he ran out of his store to look. Sure enough, there it was in full glory! With lights no less - *Yahrzeit* lights of course!

Mrs. Mertelbaum screamed that the rabbi had probably been attacked - and this was the anti-Semites way of letting the people know they had taken over the shul! Mama's butcher, Mr. Lensky, was a husky old timer. When word of this catastrophe reached him, he came out with his meat cleaver ready for action. Incidentally, by the time the word reached Lensky - the story was told that we had been invaded and pogrom was well underway!

Lensky got to the doors of shul and tried them - but they were closed. Even the Hebrew classes were cancelled that night because the building was so cold.

"*Zest* (See)- even the children aren't here!" Mrs. Mertelbaum exclaimed, adding that they had probably spirited them away as they did her whole family in Poland during the dark days of the late 1800's.

By this time a police officer saw a crowd gather in front of the shul. He walked over and asked what was going on. Nu - so how do you tell a Gentile officer?

"What happened?" He asked again, with a thick Irish brogue.

Mrs. Mertelbaum shrugged, "Nothing, we were only looking in the window."

The officer went over to the window and saw the tree in all its glory. He smiled and exclaimed, "Well, isn't that pretty! It really is decorated in good taste. You know some people over do it." He turned to walk away then called back, "Oh, a merry Chanukah to you all," and walked on into the night.

But that didn't solve anything. What was a Christmas tree doing in our shul?

Finally, Mr. Ginsberg, who operated the dry goods store on Tremont Avenue ran over to the rabbi's house. He banged on the door as if the world were coming to an end. "Reb Shlomo -Reb Shlomo -ess is Ginsberg -you can open the door!"

The rabbi's wife opened the door. Ginsberg was gasping for breath. "Vus hut getrofen? (what happened?)" she pleaded.

"Where is the rabbi?" he stammered.

Just then the rabbi came running out from his living room. "What is it?" he shouted.

"Oh, denks G-t - you're all right," Ginsberg gasped.

"Of course I'm all right. Why?" asked our Rabbi.

"The Christmas tree in your window - in your window a tree!"

The rabbi put his hand to his head and shouted, "Gevald! That was John's tree. He left it there when he went downtown to get the valve for the boiler."

The rabbi quickly put on his coat and raced back to the shul. He explained to the group standing there what had happened and everybody laughed and went home. The rabbi quickly took down the tree and decided to bring it to John's house.

So let me ask you, how often does anyone see a rabbi carrying a Christmas tree? Sure enough - who does he meet - but Mrs. Rabinowitz, who first saw the tree in his study.

"*Chas V'Shalom!*" (Oh, my goodness) she screamed once more. Now he's bringing one home!"

Her "Chas V'Shalom" rang out and half the neighbors looked out the window and saw our rabbi walking down the street with a Christmas tree under his arm.

Need I go on? John the handyman returned with the part for the boiler and after he made the repair he returned to the rabbi's office to get his tree, and of course, the tree was gone.

Who would take a Christmas tree in a shul? John looked all over for the tree - thinking the rabbi had put it away someplace. He met one of the men from the congregation and asked him if he had seen the tree.

"Yes - the rabbi was walking down the street with it before!" he explained.

He quickly ran to the rabbi's house. When he got there the Rabbi told John he had taken the tree to his house and his family was delighted with it. He thanked John for repairing the boiler and said good night.

That was all there was to the story, but by the following day the rumors in our old neighborhood were flying fast and furious. First of all, the story was so distorted that the truth was lost completely. It was such a juicy story, who wanted the truth?

About a week after Christmas we ran out of coal at the shul. Our shul was perpetually in financial difficulties. Since most of the Gentile people in the neighborhood began throwing out their Christmas trees about this time, John told the rabbi they could gather discarded trees and he would cut them up. "We could get enough heat up for your sabbath service if we let them dry out for a few days," John explained. So the rabbi and John began touring the neighborhood picking up discarded trees and then *schlepped* them to the shule.

And of course, with a tree in each hand, who did the Rabbi meet? Of course - Mrs. Rabinowitz! The poor woman, she didn't say a word, she just stared! Then she uttered to her friend "*Mistomeh* (probably) – after Christmas you can get the trees much cheaper. He's saving them for next year."

John's idea worked. The shul was warm for the *Shabbos* service, and every year thereafter we went on a Christmas tree hunt a week after the holiday – to save on coal.

REMEMBER 'TASHLICH' IN THE PARK

When we were kids we used to look forward to the High Holy Days for many reasons, but I think the main one was going to Bronx Park to watch the people say Tashlich (a holy prayer for the New Year) and throw away their sins into the Bronx River.

EVERY YEAR AFTER SERVICES ON ROSH Hashana, we would go home for dinner, then the entire family would take a walk to Bronx Park – the section where the Bronx River was once a thing of beauty.

Walking down 180th Street, with all the closed stores, you could almost tell most of the others in the neighborhood had the same idea. Everybody, dressed in their holiday finery, was walking to the park.

At the park, young and old would climb over the low

railing and walk through the grass to the water's edge to begin the prayer.

One year in particular, my little brother Berel had agreed to help a neighbor, Mrs. Rothstein, a sweet old lady in her eighties, to the park for Tashlich.

Berel, who must have been all of seven-and-a-half or eight years old, was to guide the old woman to the park. She could hardly see and barely walk. Berel wanted the mitzvah (blessing) of helping. He knew a section of the park where she could reach the river's edge without having to climb a railing.

Mrs. Rothstein hobbled along slowly and kept blessing little Berel with every step. Her son Irving was a police officer and had promised Berel he would let him see his real gun up close if he helped his mother out from time to time.

Berel and Mrs. Rothstein finally reached the water's edge. It was a long walk for such an old lady so Berel brought her to a rock near the river's edge. There she could sit down and rest before beginning the prayer.

As Mrs. Rothstein caught her breath and sat back to relax, she accidentally dropped her prayer book. It fell within a few inches of the water's edge, stuck between two rocks.

She called Berel who immediately said he would retrieve the siddur. The area in which she was sitting was extremely rocky. In order to get the book, Berel would have to jump over two treacherous rocks. No normal person would have tried it - except Berel, especially in his new suit!

Berel had climbed all over the rocks in Bronx Park every time he went to the park with his friends. To him this was no big deal.

He climbed down the side of the river's slippery rocky slope, got within a few inches of the book, and because of his brand new holiday shoes, he slipped and went - kerplunk -into the water. It wasn't too deep - maybe half a foot - but very wet.

The only problem was Berel could not climb back up

the rocky incline. Mrs. Rothstein started to scream and people from all over the park rushed to her aid. She pointed to the water and began muttering, "Save him – save the child!" Everyone ran to the river's edge and saw Berel wading in the drink. They thought he was trying to save someone who fell in. The only way Berel could get out was to walk into the middle of the stream and inch his way back to an area where there were no rocks.

One heroic man, also in the park for Tashlich, without thinking, decided to jump in to help Berel. After all, how does anyone let a seven-and-a-half year old stand in a river? There are rocks, whirlpools, and all kinds of dangers. This man jumped into the water next to Berel. But, as he jumped, he twisted his ankle and screamed out in pain.

Berel ran to his side to comfort him, but apparently the ankle was broken.

Another man, also in the park to say Tashlich eased his way down the rocks to comfort the first man and effect Berel's rescue. He slipped halfway down and hit his head on a rock. He started to bleed profusely.

Berel left the first man's side and ran to comfort the second, who was unconscious and losing blood.

Just then another man jumped in to help, then another. In a few seconds it seemed as if there were more people in the water than on the shore line. Poor Mrs. Rothstein was screaming blue murder. "Help, police, Oiving..." she yelled.

Mama and Papa, who were in the park saw the commotion and started to run over. As they got within about twenty feet, Mrs. Rothstein spotted Mama and shouted, "Berel – hut arein gefallen (had fallen in). Help, police, Oiving..."

Mama gave one scream when she saw blood on the side of the rock, where the second man had hit his head and she passed out!

Papa didn't know whether to rescue Berel, or throw rocks at him. Two women started rubbing Mama's hands as she started to pass out from the shock. Finally a police car pulled into the park, halted at the water's edge and two cops ran out to assist in the rescue. They lowered a rope to Berel, who was the only healthy one in the water, and he began helping the men who jumped in to help him, out of the water.

By this time an ambulance from Fordham Hospital had arrived at the scene and the attendants began caring for the injured. Another call went out for more ambulances. There were seven men injured with everything from a hole in the head to a broken ankle.

Finally Berel was hoisted out by the police officers. Was he surprised to see the ambulance doctor trying to revive Mama!

Papa took Berel around and hugged him. Mama came out of her faint, grabbed Berel and hugged him. You all right?" she gasped.

"Sure," he said cheerfully. Mama, with every last ounce of strength she had in her body, let go with a roundhouse swing at Berel's backside, punctuating it with, "Next time you'll play in the water?"

Mrs. Rothstein tried to explain to Mama what had happened and also to the police officers.

By this time the newspaper photographers had been notified and were on the scene. After all, how often did they send three ambulances to any place in the Bronx in those days – on Rosh Hashana no less!

They all heard how Berel helped get the men out of the water, and shoen – Berel's picture was put in the newspaper with a caption that said he was a hero.

We almost died! The newspaper didn't lie either. The reporter asked the cop what happened and the cop told him.

The cop had figured that the man with the hole in his head fell into the river and Berel saw this. Then the second man jumped in and he broke his ankle. Then the others jumped in to help the first two men who were injured.

But, as the story in the paper read, "...due to the efforts of a 7 1/2 year old youngster, the men were saved. The youth was in the park with his family when he saw a man fall in the river, he placed a prayer book between two rocks and used it as a step to reach the water without touching the slippery rocks. The book really saved the child's life as well as the lives of the injured men."

Oh, you wanna hear something funny? In all the commotion, Mrs. Rothstein never really got her siddur back.

MY BROTHER, THE PLANT SITTER

What greater acceptance could there be than when the teacher would give us a plant to take care of over a long weekend or a holiday.

WHAT A THRILL! TO BE ENTRUSTED WITH SOMEthing from the school - to be taken home and become part of our family. Incredible!

I'll never forget the time my dopey little brother Berel came home from school with a small flower pot cradled in his arms. "Ma," he shouted, "the teacher picked me from all the kids in the class to take care of the plant. She said I had to water it every day and bring it back after the holiday!"

He was so thrilled. Listen, to him it was important.

Actually, it was a mangy - looking thing - more dead than alive. What kind of a plant would a teacher give to a kid like Berel to take home?

Mama o-o-h-ed and ah-h-ed and gently placed the plant on the window sill in the kitchen.

In celebration of the occasion, Mama took a bottle of seltzer from the little box we had hanging just outside the kitchen window, that acted as our refrigerator and offered Berel a seltzer cocktail - milk and seltzer!

"And just think, she picked me over everybody else!" He couldn't get over the thrill.

Then, as he took the bottle of seltzer to place back in the window box, in his excitement, he accidentally rubbed up against the plant - and that dismal plant went sailing down five stories to the courtyard where it smashed into a million pieces!

Gevald! What a disaster!

Berel and Mama quickly ran down the five flights of stairs to the yard as neighbors started to gather when they heard the explosion-like noise the flower pot made!

When Mama and Berel reached the yard, they saw the plant was just about destroyed. The broken pot had severed the small stem and the leaves were crushed by the earth and clay debris.

Berel started to cry uncontrollably.

"She trusted me with the plant - and now it's smashed!" he cried.

Mama started to gather up the soil in a newspaper and picked up the remains of the plant. "Don't worry *tateleh*," she consoled, Mama will fix it so that the teacher will never know!"

"She'll kill me!" he whined. "She said I should take good care of it!"

"Don't worry - don't worry - Mama will go to school with you on Monday. Don't worry!" Mama explained as she walked up the five flights. "*Luz ess zein far der kapora!*" (Let it be for the evil ones).

Once in the house she laid out what was left of the plant on a piece of newspaper. It was apparent that all the fixing in the world would never put that poor plant back together again.

Berel was crying real tears. Mama asked me to go to the park with Berel to get some soil. Meanwhile, she would canvas the neighbors to see who had a flower pot.

I took Berel to the park as he continued to cry. We took along the ice box *shissel* to carry the earth home. When we got to the park we went to a section where beautiful little plants had been planted.

As we started to dig up some soil with our hands, I was certain the Parks Department wouldn't mind if we sort of gave one of their little plants a good home. So we reached over near a beautiful bush and took one of the little seedlings.

We quickly covered the shissel with newspaper and raced for the house. When we got home, Mama was all smiles. On the kitchen table was a flower pot – an exact replica of the one that fell out of the window.

"*Zest!*" Mama exclaimed, "Mermelstein had a pot and we'll put the plant in the flower pot and we'll stick in some of the old plant that looks like it might have a little more life left in it – and also the plant you shouldn't have taken from the park and *shoen*! The teacher will never know the difference."

Mama gently washed off the roots of the decapitated plant, then placed the soil in the pot and gently tucked the new little plant in the center.

I'll tell you this – it looked a heck of a lot better than the monstrosity Berel brought home. This time she placed the pot on the window sill in the living room.

Berel watered the plant with mixed emotions. He knew it wasn't the same plant and the thought that the teacher would discover the fraud, ate away at him.

That night he almost cried himself to sleep. The following day when he went out to play with his friends they insisted on coming up to our house to see the plant the teacher had entrusted to Berel. After all, he was sort of a celebrity. But, Berel kept making one excuse after another not to bring the kids into the house.

The long weekend finally passed and the little plants looked like they were thriving. Monday morning arrived and it was raining cats and dogs.

Mama told Berel she preferred that he not take the plant to school in the rain. She gave him a note for the teacher telling her that when it stopped raining he would bring the plant.

Sure enough, it rained the next day too. And the third day it poured.

By the fourth day – the sun was shining and the weather was delightfully warm.

Berel got up, looked at the sun, and his heart fell. He was certain the teacher would discover the switch and was almost in tears as Mama gave him the plant.

"If the teacher says something," Mama began, "tell her I decided to fix it up a little bit!"

Berel arrived at school with the plant in one piece. When he handed the plant to the teacher she took one look at it and smiled. The little seedling we had picked up in the park was starting to sport tiny new leaves.

"What is this?" she exclaimed with joy. "New leaves? My goodness, I never thought that plant would even survive the weekend!"

Berel beamed!

The teacher looked at the plant and the pot curiously and commented, "I can see you even washed the pot around. It almost looks new! You even added a little more soil! Now, that's what I call taking care of a plant. In fact, I notice you even cut down the old plant a little so that it would have more room to grow! Who taught you all this?

Berel beamed from ear to ear. He was bursting with pride, but thank G-d, he kept his mouth shut.

The teacher gently placed the plant on the window, and even called in the teacher next door to show her how the little plant had suddenly come back to life.

"Look how beautiful this child took care of this plant

in only a week!" she exclaimed with pride.

Well, let me tell you something - Berel was on cloud nine!

Then she turned to Berel and said, "Because you did so well with the plant I am going to excuse you from the arithmetic homework today!"

If she had given him a million dollars she couldn't have given him a better present!

As the end of the day drew near she turned to Berel and asked, "I have another little plant that isn't doing too well. Do you think you can take it home for a few days to give it the love and care you gave the other? Maybe this will grow in your house like the other? I'm going to the hospital this afternoon to tell my father, who is a doctor, the magic you performed."

Berel stood up with pride and accepted the plant.

Meanwhile, around three o'clock Mama was looking out the window waiting for Berel to come home from school, expecting the worst! After all, *takeh* if the teacher discovered the switch she was just the kind to give him both barrels. An angel this teacher wasn't! Sure enough, as Berel turned the corner, Mama saw him carrying the plant in his arms.

Gevald! "The teacher sent him home with the plant demanding her other one!" Mama thought.

By the time Berel came upstairs with the new plant, Mama was at the door expecting the worst. But, as the door opened, he walked in all smiles and announced, "We gotta go to the park again - she liked the other one so much - she gave me a'nudder one!"

Mama was ready to strangle him!

Did you tell her what happened?" she asked.

"Didn't have to - she never knew the difference!" he exclaimed all smiles, munching on a crust of pumpernickel that had been literally smeared with a clove of garlic and sprinkled with salt.

When I came home from school Mama looked at me

and said softly, "Take a walk by the park - we need more soil."

I knew already! I took the *shissel* once more and an old soup spoon and with jerky little Berel in tow - went to the park. We dug out a little more soil and adopted another little plant that looked so lonely, near the same bush. It had such beautiful green leaves.

As we walked out of the park, a police officer saw the two of us with the shissel of soil and the plant and stopped us.

"What in the world do you think you are doing?" the officer shouted. "You can't take plants from the park! That's against the law!"

I started to *funfer* (stutter). After all, what could I say? I was caught red-handed. But then Berel spoke up: "It's for my teacher," he began.

"Your teacher?" questioned the cop, "Where is your teacher?"

"She's in the hospital..." but before he could finish the sentence the officer put his hand on Berel's shoulder and smiled, "That's okay little fellow - I understand! But you really shouldn't be taking any plants out of the park. Go ahead, and wish her well!"

We ran home like two little thieves. Berel was all smiles.

Mama quickly planted the little seedling in the pot with the other mangy-looking plant and it really looked great - the little green shoot really added a lot to the plant.

Night time came and Berel went to sleep. But, around ten - thirty that night, Mama's neighbor's daughter, Sarah Skolnik stopped in to give Mama something her mother had borrowed earlier in the day. She took one look at the plant on the kitchen table and started to get hysterical with laughter.

"What's so funny?" Mama questioned.

"In all my years I..." and she couldn't go on.

"Tell me," Mama pleaded.

She began once more, taking a closer look at the little shoot we had picked up in the park.

"Why in the world would anyone want to plant Poison Ivy in a flower pot?" she was bursting with laughter.

Mama didn't know what to say.

Sarah left in hysterics!

Mama didn't have the heart to tell Berel, and left the plant the way we replanted it.

The following morning Berel took the plant back to school and Mama threatened to break his head if he ever brought another plant home again. She also made certain that he and the other children shouldn't touch the leaves – because she said, "They might die."

So Berel brought the plant to school and his teacher was impressed once more.

Berel was excused from homework again – but – G–d knows if Sarah was right! Of course, I am certain she was wrong – because Berel passed everything that term. Oh, I should point out, his teacher was out of school for few weeks with an "allergy" shortly after the plants were delivered – but, I'm sure the plants had nothing to do with it – or did they?

THE TROLLEY CARS

In our day, whenever you got off the trolley, there was always someone who would ask if you had an extra transfer to spare. In those days transfers were free and if someone got a transfer they could save five cents on a trolley ride. Listen, we were fighting poverty - our own!

THE TROLLEY CARS OF YESTERDAY ARE museum pieces today. Who doesn't remember seeing the world flash by from the back of a trolley car? When we were kids - for a nickel you could travel the whole of Tremont Avenue to a new world - the West Bronx!

The trolley cars of our day had character - they never grew old - they never changed. Of course, some creaked a little more than others, but who cared? For a nickel - you saw the whole world.

As kids, when Mama would take us to visit a relative, it was a ritual to run to the back of the trolley and sit at the disabled rear controls as the driver was running the car at the front. During the freezing winter days, there was a warmth that came from the heaters under the seats that beat anything today's busses have to offer.

In the summer, they used special trolleys that had open sides. All that was between you and the outside world that was scooting by was a little wire grating. That was our air conditioning! There was no gasoline smell, only the hum as the electricity surged through the motor to put the wheels in motion.

The motorman who drove that trolley stood at the front of the car like a sea captain at the helm of his ship. He stood there proudly navigating the curves in the tracks tugging at the little bell-cord near him to warn cars in his path. Our motormen knew the neighborhood. They rode back and forth on the same routes and knew every bump in the track. They issued transfers with a smile. They knew every intersection and every interlocking track that converged on their route. I remember a friend of mine lived in a section where he took a trolley to school and always got a transfer. After school he would walk a block to an intersection where he would use the transfer on another line to get home!

In the evenings, the motorman on a trolley would drop a little curtain behind him to block off the reflection of the lights in the car. That brown wrinkled curtain danced back and forth as the car swayed along its merry route. For years we wondered what the motorman was doing behind that curtain!

On cold nights, as you stood on a corner, the most wonderful and welcome sight you could see was that single flickering light swaying in the distance. It was like an old friend with a smile. Even when you couldn't see the light because of turns in the tracks you could hear the sound of the approaching car from the hum of the wheels against the rails.

That deep tenor voice - like sound coming from the gears was always there. It wasn't annoying, it was comforting.

The trolley cars of our day really weren't speed demons that raced along the track. They did an average of ten miles an hour. As the trolly rolled down the tracks, as kids, we imagined we were in a Buck Rogera rocket ship and felt as if we were about to go into orbit. It was a gentle rolling. What kid can ever forget those friendly yellow and red cars with their woven straw seats that left their waffle-like patterns on our knees as we looked out the window - watching the world go by. And then we suddenly grew up and took the trolley to school every day by ourself. This was sheer independence.

Who can forget the kids who hitched rides on the back of the trolleys? They were the daredevils of our day. And how many of them went home with bruises and sprains as they jumped off the cars running from the motorman.

I think the best part of the trolley ride was reaching the end of the line and watching the conductor's specialty number. He would pull down the electric pole that was attached to the electric line above the car with such great dignity as he switched the power source from the front of the car to the back.

The motorman stood erect and firm in his dark blue uniform. He would tug at the trolley line that was attached to that conduction pole. With confident dead aim he would release the line and the little pulley would make contact with the thin electric wire stretched overhead. The subtle "click-click-click" of the converter under the car signaled the motorman that the contact was good.

It was indeed a ceremony comparable to London's changing of the guard.

The conductor would then walk through the car reversing the backs of the seats with such deliberatness and an air of importance. He was the commander of his ship. When we learned that a sea captain could marry a couple at sea - we often wondered if a conductor or motorman could marry a couple aboard his trolley, in an emergency of course!

Then as we grew older and more modern trolley cars came into being, we almost resented them. I remember being so jealous of the cars that ran along Coney Island Avenue in Brooklyn. We saw them when we visited relatives. They went like bullets – racing along the street at twenty-five miles an hour! I almost felt like a traitor abandoning our old yellow and red cars of the Bronx. Those cars were more than a means of transportation, they were a part of our childhood.

Who can forget the fare box? A fare was dropped in the coin box and a little bell rang, a little meter would register the fare and you could even see the passenger counting meter from your seat. We always wondered how they managed to make a living from so few nickels – after all, the trolleys didn't run on love – they used electricity! And how Mama would always say, "Don't worry for them, they make more money than your father!"

On Sundays if we had nothing to do, for a nickel we would ride from one end of the Bronx to the other, back and forth, all for the same nickel. The scenery didn't change but the people did – but who looked at the scenery? We looked at people.

When a section of track would wear out – it was always a thrill to watch the street crews change the track without losing a second from the trolley schedules. They would skillfully switch the car to the opposite track and it would chug along its merry way once more.

On the snowiest days – the trolleys didn't wait for the snow plows – they cut their path through the snow and ice with their little sandbox pipes spewing sand in front of their little steel wheels. That sand gave the cars perfect traction and they jogged along even in the worst kinds of weather.

A ride on a trolley was a carefree ride. If you were in a hurry you took a train. If you were interested in relaxing you took a trolley.

When my sister got married and moved to Pittsburgh,

She lived in a corner house on Negley Avenue just where a trolley car made a turn onto the main street. That trolley would squeal violently as it turned the corner. The trolley car company even had a man with a grease stick to lubricate the tracks during the day – but it really didn't help much.

In the daytime you couldn't hear much of the squeal over the clatter of the general noises. However, at night when all was still, the squeal became a friendly sound as the motorman would deliberately slow down the car to minimize the noise. It really didn't minimize the noise, it just put the squeal in a different musical key. That squeal was ear-splitting – like a soprano at the opera.

After a while a group of people in the neighborhood complained to the Mayor's office to discontinue the trolley at night because they said the noises kept them awake. But after two weeks of the car not running at night those very same people asked that the car be put back – they said they missed the noise so much that they couldn't fall asleep. Knowing life was going on outside their homes and that someone was there in those late hours was a comforting thought.

But the trolley is now part of the past generation. It is part of yesterday's world – part of an adventure – an experience, a happening that is now extinct in New York City.

MR. SKOLNIK,
THE ASSISTANT DOCTOR

The patient would tell Dr. Skolnik's father what was bothering him and the old timer would say with a smile on his face, "I had the same thing a short time ago and my son Leo cured me in a few days. He's some boy!"

LET ME TELL YOU SOMETHING, THE DOCTORS they have today aren't like the ones we had when we were kids. I remember a young doctor in our old neighborhood who had an office in a small private house just a few blocks from where we lived.

The doctor's father, a retired painter, was like a fixture on the front porch sitting in his rocking chair. He would sit on that porch winter and summer just enjoying people, waving to a few or just smiling as friends passed by. In the winter he would be bundled up in a heavy wool coat and in the summer relax with a thin sports shirt with a hot glass of tea always in his hand.

Whenever a patient came to visit the doctor's office the old timer would greet them. He would be a sort of sounding board for their misery. He would rise slowly from his chair, adjust his glasses, and as he walked them into the waiting room, would even take their pulse. He would smile as they sat down and would say confidently, "To me it doesn't sound bad. Wait, my son will fix you up."

Whether you were sick or not – you immediately felt better. You felt you were in the hands of experience.

The old timer played an important role in his son's practice. Should anybody come in with a broken arm or leg, the old timer would have the honor of mixing the plaster for the cast. After all, who could mix plaster better than a retired painter? And did that old timer feel important!

The old man played the role perfectly. He would put on a white jacket just like his son's and assist in the application of the plaster. As a matter of fact, he looked and almost sounded more like a doctor than his son.

Mr. Skolnik was a warm and kindly old soul who had a great bedside manner. When he noticed a patient in the waiting room who had anxiety written all over their face, he would sit next to them and talk softly. No matter what the malady was – old Mr. Skolnik said he had the same thing just a few weeks before and his son cured him.

Sometimes a woman would come in with a woman's problem – but this did not stop the old timer. He would commiserate by telling the patient his sister had the same problem and his son the doctor cured her in a few days.

No matter what it was, from athlete's foot to hangnail, Mr. Skolnik would say he had the same problem and his son had cured him. He was indeed so proud.

As I think back, I wonder how many people really came to see Dr. Skolnik and how many came to talk with his father. I'll never forget the time Mama had taken me to Dr. Skolnik's office when the doctor was out on a house call. As we waited, the door burst open and a woman in near panic holding her baby in her arms rushed into the room. The child had just swallowed a button and was turning blue from suffocation. The old man quickly grabbed the baby, ran into his son's office and in a split second the button was out. The baby was crying but breathing normally. How that woman blessed him! Just after the crisis his son returned and the woman told the doctor what had happened. The son was very angry and admonished his father severely. "Pa, you're practicing medicine without a license!"

The old man took off his white coat in anger and shouted back, "I didn't need a license when you swallowed a cufflink when you were a baby! I used the very same medicine! I held you upside down and gave you a good smack in the right place! You think you know everything? Everything - you know?"

Dr. Skolnik swallowed hard and saw that he had hurt the old timer. Really, there was nothing he could say or do that was going to change the old timer's ways.

There was a touch of irony to the incident. For months afterward, when the woman came to the doctor she would demand that old Mr. Skolnik be in the room with his son for the examination. She would zing the doctor with: "I trust you Dr. Skolnik, but I just want to make certain you do everything right. Please let you father watch!"

If a patient had a cold, and the son would prescribe a certain medicine, as the patient left, the old timer would follow the woman to the door and whisper, "Listen, *gib der kiend ah bissel* (give the child a little) chicken soup - it wouldn't hurt! Ah little chicken soup wouldn't hurt the child."

The woman would leave beaming, feeling she not only had the services of the doctor, but "ah specialist" as well.

There were times when patients would leave after a visit, they would go over to the old timer as he sat on the porch, show him the prescription his son had given them and then ask softly, "Tell me Mr. Skolnik, *ich dof dos*? (Do

I really need this?)

The old timer would adjust his glasses and look at the prescription carefully that was usually written in Latin and chemical terms and say knowingly, "This is a very special prescription. My son doesn't give this to everyone."

The patient would leave feeling so confident the "specialist" had confirmed the prescription.

There was another time I shall never forget. A man came running into Dr. Skolnik's office. Apparently his mother, who was well into her eighties, was having a heart attack.

Dr. Skolnik was at the hospital on an emergency. Mr. Skolnik called his son at the hospital and informed him of the emergency.

"I'll be right over," his son said. "Tell him to go back to the house. I'll meet him there."

Old Mr. Skolnik went back to the house with Mr. Hockmeyer to see what he could do for the old lady until Dr. Skolnik arrived. When he got there, it seemed as if the old lady was gasping her last. Still in that white jacket he wore so proudly, old Mr. Skolnik sat down next to the old lady, adjusted his glasses and held her pulse. He spoke softly to her and as she appeared to doze off, he began reciting Psalms softly.

About twenty minutes later, Dr. Skolnik arrived. The worst was over. The old woman had come through the crisis clutching the hand of old Mr. Skolnik.

Dr. Skolnik examined the old lady and gave her an injection to make her feel a little more comfortable. Then they both left.

For weeks afterward, whenever doctor Skolnik made a house call he had to take his father along. And to this very day no one knows whether it was Dr. Skolnik's medicines that kept the old lady alive or Mr. Skolnik's bedside manner and warm understanding.

When Dr. Skolnik was out of the office his father used to take the phone calls. He would answer the phone with,

"Dr. Skolnik's office. The doctor is not in. He is on an emergency."

The patient would tell the old timer what the problem was and then old Mr. Skolnik would reply, "I'll tell the doctor as soon as he comes in - meanwhile, take an enema - it wouldn't hurt."

When Dr. Skolnik would come back to his office and hear what the father had told the patient he would turn green. "Pa..." the son began, "You can't tell every patient to take an enema. Sometimes an enema can hurt a person!"

The old timer was indignant. "An enema can't hurt nothing!"

"Pa, you don't understand," his son would plead.

"Listen my son, when you got sick I always gave you an enema and it didn't hurt you. Maybe it hurt your brain a little bit - but inside it wouldn't hurt!" The old man would walk away and pout.

It got to the point where the son had to hire a nurse to mind the office when he was away. And don't think it didn't affect his practice. If a patient came into the office and the nurse wanted to take a medical history the patient would walk out! They insisted that the old timer take the history.

It was riot to watch the old timer strike back. The son would send his patients to the drug store for a prescription. The old man would sit on the porch and tell them, "Take a seltzer - and give a good *grepse* (belch) " he would say seriously then add, "And then a good glesseleh of tea –dot's all. Dot's wot I take!"

Nine out of ten times they would throw away the prescription and do what the old timer said - after all, they figured if that's what a doctor's father did, why shouldn't they?

When a poor family would visit his son and they didn't have the money for the office visit the old timer would hand them the money on the porch and say, "*Gib ess tzu mine zindeleh* (Give this to my little son) give him the money so he shouldn't feel bad."

The son must have known but he didn't let on. It made the old timer feel good. After all, the money didn't go far – just to the next room. Besides, some of those old timers even paid the old man back.

Despite all the wonderful things that old mad did, the one thing we remembered him for was his measles medicine. Whenever a kid in the neighborhood would come down with the measles the old timer would visit the family and give the youngster his very own medicine. Actually it was a bag of rock candy that we loved to munch on. After all, we all reasoned, how bad could it be if it came from a doctor's father?

THE LOWER EAST SIDE

Mama and Papa's America was the Lower East Side of New York City. This was the melting pot. To the millions of immigrants who came to these shores, America was not "The Promised Land" - New York City was!

AS THE BOATS PULLED INTO NEW YORK Harbor, Ellis Island became "a suburb of America." How did so many foreign sounding names wind up as typical Anglo-Saxon names? Blame it on the immigration officials! It was here immigration officials, who could not understand the foreign dialects, selected arbitrary names for the immigrants. For example: my father and his brothers came over from Russia on the same boat, but each of them wound up with different last names. The guards couldn't understand Russian - so when Papa gave his last name which was Farful in Russia, it came out quite different. In fact, one brother wound up with the name as Farrel, and another, Goldstein, when they came over. *Nu.*

So how did we wind up with the last name of Fine when it was originally Farful? When the immigration agent was interviewing Papa, Papa kept talking in Russian and the agent did not understand. He simply kept saying, "Yup, that's fine young man. Yup, that's fine."

When Papa came to the next agent the only English word he knew was 'fine'. So when the agent asked, "What's your name?" Papa answered with the only English word he knew, which was 'fine'.

When the immigrants landed in New York City they went to stay with *lantzleit,* or friends from the old country. Each group stayed together. They voluntarily created their own ghettos. That was their strength. Each helped the other. They laughed together and they cried together. If one of the immigrants managed to get a pushcart - he was considered a capitalist! He was in business for himself. Now he had the privilege of working sixteen to twenty hours a day. But he was his own boss. If he bought a second pushcart for a brother or relative - he was considered *ungeshtoped.* (loaded). What these old timers escaped from in Europe did not exist in America. But they longed for the culture of their homeland. Each brought a part of that culture to America.

And don't forget, all the immigrants weren't Jewish! Little Italy sprung up on Mulberry Street. Chinatown transported the Far East to Mott Street - where it still stands today. Our people took over Scammel Street, Essex and Delancey Streets. Each block was like part of the old world. You heard more languages in a single block than you could hear in a lifetime of touring Europe.

Some courageous souls broke out of the ghetto and moved to a suburb called Brooklyn. But it was the same in spirit. I'll never forget one family who lived near us. How they happened to *volger* (wander) into our neighborhood I'll never know. They spoke Italian - but after three months that whole family spoke Yiddish like it was their native tongue. In fact, Mr. Vertelli took off on all Jewish holidays. And don't think the ability to understand and speak Yiddish didn't play an important part in their lives. Mr. Vertelli got a job in the garment center as a foreman because he could speak and understand Italian. Most of the finishers in the garment center were Italian. Yet Mr. Vertelli could converse with the customers in Yiddish.

I'll never forget the time Mrs. Vertelli was looking for a coat for her daughter and Mr. Vertelli sent her up to a shop on the same block. Mrs. Vertelli and her daughter were shown a few garments and spoke Italian in front of the salesman. "Ma," Mrs. Vertelli's daughter exclaimed in Italian, "If he lets us have the coat for twenty-five dollars it will be a real buy - see how much he wants."

Mrs. Vertelli turned to the salesman and asked in broken English with the Italian accent, "Quanta costa? How mucha you wanta for thisa coat?"

The salesman smiled and called to his boss in the back. "Hymie, *vifull faren* green coat *far der Talener?*" (How much for the green coat for the Italian?)

From the back the boss called out in Yiddish, "Oiving, *freck zay feretzik toller - Uber, if zay vet leufen avec - gib ess tzu zay far fiftzen toller.*" (Irving, ask them forty dollars, but if they want to go, give it to them for fifteen dollars).

The salesman smiled pleasantly, certain they didn't understand what was just said in Yiddish and said, "Since you are Vertelli's wife, my boss will give it to you for his cost, forty dollars! And dot's strictly wholesale!"

Mrs. Vertelli turned and snapped, "Thatsa too much! We are going som-a-place else!"

As they started walking toward the door of the showroom, the salesman chased after them and exclaimed, "Look, I'll give it to you for thirty dollars - I'll give up my commission!"

Mrs. Vertelli continued to walk toward the elevator with the salesman pleading behind her.

Finally she stopped and turned to the salesman. In perfect Yiddish she snapped, *"Far vust hust du gefreckt meir dreitzik toller ven der boss hut gezukt fiftzen toller?"* (Why did you ask me thirty dollars when the boss had asked fifteen dollars?)

The salesman swallowed hard. He nearly choked! Meanwhile the boss who was still in the back called out, "Oiving - *gib zay der coat faren tzen toller - ess hut ah tzerioner lining!*" (Irving, give them the coat for ten dollars, it has a torn lining!)

And Oiving the poor salesman shouted back, "Hymie, *far mach der pisk! Zay vaysin vee tzu hahndlin besser foon dier!*" (Hymie, shut up! They know how to deal better than you!)

Hymie turned to Mrs. Vertelli and sighed, *"Nem der coat for ten dollars - it was worth the experience! Trug ess gezunteh heit!*" (Wear it in good health!)

The coat was wrapped up and everyone began to laugh - except the boss because Oiving gave Ms. Vertelli a coat without the torn lining!

Let me tell you something - there is nothing around today like the old time businessmen. I'll never forget Mr. Finkelstein who ran the "Boys and Men's Swanky Suits" establishment on Delancey Street. This old timer was a frail little fellow with a huge hearing aid always pinned to his shirt only you never saw the earpiece in his ear. He had perfect hearing. It was simply a prop!

When a customer would walk in and select a suit, Finkelstein would excuse himself and shout to his partner in the back, "Moe, how much for the Glenn Plaid suit - the good line?"

And the partner would call back, "Forty-five dollars - that's plenty suit..."

Finkelstein would cup his ear as if straining to hear, then turn to the customer and shrug, "My partner says twenty- five dollars! You know it looks like a forty-five dollar suit we used to carry! But he just called out twenty-five, you heard him! So that's the price!"

The customer, thinking he was really getting a steal because he heard the partner call out forty-five dollars would whisper, "Wrap it up immediately - I'll have the cuffs made on the outside! Here's the twenty-five dollars." And then he'd run like a thief! Actually Finkelstein sold a ten dollar suit for twenty five-dollars.

And don't think this kind of business sense was exclusive in the garment industry. In those days how many stores would advertise, "Eggs, 88 cents a dozen. Slightly cracked - 65 cents a dozen."

The women would stand in line and plead for the cracked eggs, especially on Friday. After all, what difference did it make if the eggs were cracked - they would go into a cake the same day.

The truth of the matter was that the 65 cent cracked eggs were really 55 cent eggs that the boss would slightly crack every Friday morning so his customers would think they were getting a bargain!

This was the America of the old world. But don't sell today's businessmen short. Have you seen how many children's stores are selling mini-dresses to woman customers as "children's clothing" which is non-taxable in some communities?

Nu - like I said in the beginning, it's a new world.

RESIDENT SPECIALISTS

Who knew from Blue Cross or hospitalization in any form?
If we got sick, what chicken soup didn't cure - the neighbors
did. Let me ask you, in those years, who called a doctor unless
you were having a baby?

HEN WE WERE KIDS, WE HAD A NEIGHBOR, Mr. Spielberg. Spielberg worked in the garment center as a cutter and always boasted that he never had a sick day in his life. One day he got up in the morning and the whole left side of his face was almost paralyzed.

The first thing he did was run down to Mrs. Mermelstein, the "resident physician" in our building. What she couldn't diagnose wasn't worth having. *Takeh!*

"To me-e-e," she drawled like a specialist, "*Ess kooked ous vee ah* (it looks like) a stroke!"

"Gevald!" screamed Spielberg, "How do I come to *ah* stroke? I never had a sick day in my life. How do I come to *ah* stroke?"

"Listen," Mrs. Mermelstein counseled, "who says it's hereditary?"

Spielberg was beside himself. "Nu – so what can be done?"

Mrs. Mermelstein continued her cooking and casually commented, "You have to thank G-d it was only ah stroke – Ga- fa-bit it could have been a heart attack? You should be thankful! Oy, are you lucky! Getting a heart attack in your sleep could be dangerous. But ah stroke – listen, it could have been worse." She spoke so professionally we always had a sneaky feeling she must have been at least a nurse in the Civil War.

Spielberg wasn't as entirely happy as Mrs. Mermelstein. Listen, a stroke is a terrible thing. So right away he decided to go to a specialist – Mrs. Sachman. Mrs. Sachman was only called upon for very special consultations. She lived on the first floor in the front. The reason that she was considered a specialist was that she was a hypochondriac and would run to a doctor two or three times a week. Everyone figured she knew more than even Mrs. Mermelstein, who was usually good for small head colds, athlete's foot, and occasionally removing splinters from fingers.

Spielberg walked into Mrs. Sachman's apartment. She took one look at Spielberg and announced with complete reassurance – "You got the same thing my Ginger had just last year."

"*Ah* stroke?" questioned Spielberg.

"Who said stroke? You got an impacted nerve," she replied with the assurance of an authority.

She leaned over, picked up her reddish brown cat and held it in front of Spielberg. "*Zest* – today she's perfect. My Ginger is one hundred percent p'ufect..." and she cuddled the little creature to her face with so much love.

"It happens usually before a cat gives birth," she

declared.

"Who's pregnant? shouted Spielberg. "I'm not even married! Listen, I don't like to advertise – but I'm still a boy! True, I'm forty-two years old – but listen –.""

Mrs. Sachman began to laugh. "What can I tell you? All I said was that you have the same thing my Ginger had and she gave birth to kittens a few weeks later. *Eppis* (sometimes) *ah* nerve gets twisted – or they worry a lot. You know! Maybe you have problems in your business?"

Spielberg shrugged innocently, "Danks Gut – everything is ho kay. How does an impacted nerve come to me? Mermelstein said it was a stroke."

"*Vus Vaist* Mermelstein? What does she know? She looks at a few sore throats – I at least run to the vet – and they tell me all these things. The best thing you should do is stay off meat and eat only raw fish."

"Fish?" questioned Spielberg.

"Fish!" retorted Mrs. Sachman. "Dot is wot the doctor told me to do for Ginger. Only fish. But it must be fresh, raw – not cooked."

"Not cooked?" screamed Spielberg. "For a cat yes – but for a human – who eats raw fish?"

"Listen, you don't want to listen to me – so go back to Mermelstein – let it be ah stroke. But, I'm telling you it's an impacted nerve."

Spielberg walked out dejected. On his way up to his own apartment he bumped into Mr. Goldman, our druggist. Goldman was usually considered to be "like" a doctor –after all, how far from a doctor could a druggist be? He knew all the medicines. Goldman took one look at Spielberg and shrugged, "Bell's Palsy."

"What?" shrieked Spielberg. "Bell's what?"

"Dot's wot they call Bell's Palsy – you got it!" Goldman exclaimed.

"Wait! Wait!" shouted Spielberg, "What does that mean?"

Goldman, almost snobbishly halted at the top of the

stairs like a doctor in the movies and replied, "You got it – dot's what it means."

Goldman reached for the keys in his pocket and Spielberg ran to his side. "Nu, so tell me what must I do? Is it dangerous? It's not a stroke? It's not an impacted nerve?"

"A wot?" questioned Goldman. "An impacted nerve? Who told you dot?"

"Mrs. Sachman," Spielberg replied.

"Listen, if you have an impacted nerve you go to ah dentist not a veterinarian? Wot does Sachman know? If you're not a cat or dog – she doesn't know," Goldman sounded almost angry.

"But Mermelstein said it's ah stroke," Spielberg interrupted.

"Listen," Goldman began, "Mrs. Mermelstein is a very nice lady. Bakes a delicious kugel – but when it comes to diagnosing a Bell's Palsy – she doesn't know. Take it from me – dot's wot you got. Listen, why don't you go to see a doctor?"

"But what could a doctor tell me?" Spielberg questioned. "After all, it's not like I was sick. I feel all right. It's just that my face is a little *fakrimpt*. (twisted). So long as it isn't ah stroke who cares?"

Goldman was getting more and more annoyed. Please go to ah doctor, let him diagnose. I should not even have said wot I did."

"Tell me, what can I do for it?" Spielberg persisted.

"Do for it?" Goldman questioned. "Listen, there is nothing you can do for it. In a few weeks it will go away as mysteriously as it came. But do me a favor – go to a doctor. Please!"

He slammed the door and Spielberg quickly ran back to Mrs. Mermelstein.

"Goldman says it's what they call Bell's Palsy, and will clear up in a few weeks. Did you ever hear of such a thing?"

Mrs. Mermelstein, not to be outdone by a "mere" druggist snapped with a smile – "Sure, who hasn't heard of

Gell's Palsy?"

"That's Bell's Palsy," corrected Spielberg.

"You heard him wrong it's really like I set – Gell's Palsy. I see it all the time. Just put hot compresses to the face and it will go away. It's like Mumps!" Mrs. Mermelstein had gathered her composure and was talking like a doctor once more.

Spielberg felt better that he got a confirming opinion. He quickly ran down to Mrs. Sachman and told her what Goldman had said, and how Mrs. Mermelstein had confirmed it!

"Dot's exactly wot I set!" Mrs. Sachman exclaimed. "When a nerve gets impacted dot's wot they call Mell's Palsy."

"No – no," corrected Spielberg – "That's Bell's Palsy."

"When a cat has it, it's called Mell's Palsy," she corrected him.

Spielberg shook his head in confusion. "There's so much you have to know to be ah doctor! *Gevald!* Am I glad I have such good friends."

"But," replied Mrs. Sachman, "you should put cold compresses on your cheek and eat raw fish."

"Goldman didn't say anything about raw fish," he replied innocently.

"Listen," she replied with a smug smile, "do you think Goldman would tell you everything for nothing? He works hand in hand with the doctors. When they give you ah medicine it's a sale for Goldman and the doctor gets his fee. But wot do you think is in those medicines? Vitamins – just plain vitamins like you get from food. So why pay for medicine when you can get it direct from the food?"

Spielberg was so appreciative when he left. On the way to shul for the evening prayers he ran into Dr. Perlman. Dr. Perlman greeted him warmly and looked at Spielberg's face. "Oh, my – why don't you stop in my office and let me take a look at that," the doctor said.

Spielberg was all smiles. "When I feel a little better I'll

stop in. Don't worry doc – I already know what it is and how to treat it."

The doctor looked up in surprise. Who did you go to?"

A little embarrassed, Spielberg began to *funfer*.

"Mermelstein – I bet!" snapped doctor Perlman.

"Listen, she told me everything," Spielberg said almost in anger.

"And if she's wrong?" questioned Perlman, "then what?"

"Listen Perlman – do you think I would take one opinion? I also went to Sachman."

"*Oichut* (also) *ah* doctor?" snapped Perlman. "You better stop in my office tonight after supper," and he stormed away.

But Spielberg still had faith in his medical cadre. For supper he had a piece of raw fish and put on alternately hot and cold compresses. Then, he went to Dr. Perlman's office.

Perlman diagnosed the illness as an infection of the seventh facial nerve – also referred to as Bell's Palsy – and eating a ton of raw fish with hot and cold compresses wouldn't change the fact that it would take him about four to six weeks to recover.

Despite the advice of Dr. Perlman, Spielberg still sneaked in a piece of raw fish occasionally and did continue to apply hot compresses one day and cold he next. And sure enough by the end of the fifth week his face straightened up.

"*Nu*," he asked Mama, "so who was right? Maybe it would have cleared up if I didn't eat the fish or put on the compresses? Who knows? Perlman didn't give me any medicine – so I ask you – who was right?

And the truth of the matter is – takeh who was right?

The years have passed and Mrs. Mermelstein's "practice" has dwindled with all the Medicare and Medicaid available today. But, now when she gets calls from old friends she is far more professional. She tells them, "Listen, take two aspirins and if you don't feel better in the morning – go to ah doctor – I don't make house calls anymore!"

THE IMPORTANT PEOPLE

Remember the people we thought were so important when we were little kids? Next to the President of the United States, we thought our superintendent was the most important.

O N RAINY DAYS WE'D PLAY IN THE HALLWAY and suddenly the superintendent would run up the stairs and shout, "Get out of the halls or I'll disposess you all!" How we trembled! How important we thought he was. After all, he and the landlord were friends!

And remember another important person – the man who took the tickets at the movies? What authority, we thought. No one could enter the movies unless they went up to him and gave him a ticket. Even today when I go to a movie I get a slight tremor when I pass the ticket-taker. Usually when I buy tickets I walk straight ahead because I'm

---

anxious to see the movie! But, my wife lags behind. She has to look at the pictures in the lobby. So, the man tears up the tickets and I keep walking. Once inside the theater I usually find my wife is still in the lobby looking at the pictures coming in the next week. So, how will she get in - will the fella who tore up the tickets remember I gave him two? And I worry. But somehow she gets in - he always remembers!

When we were quite small we envied the kids who folded programs for the local motion picture theater. How important we thought they were! Think of it - folding programs in the manager's office! They could hear the movie all the time they folded programs! And on top of this privilege the manager gave each one a whole pass, good only weekdays, for folding programs for three hours. In those days a whole ticket was a dime!

And how we envied the kids who were hired by the newsstand dealer on the corner of Southern Boulevard and Tremont Avenue every Saturday night. Their job was to insert the colored comics in the Sunday papers. What authority! What a privilege - they told us they were able to read the comics even before the news trucks dropped off the late newspapers. They even got as much as fifteen cents for a whole night's work even in the most miserable freezing weather. We, like little dopes, would stand a whole night with them for nothing, hoping one would sprain a finger so we could take over. Who did it for money? It was the authority that job suggested.

And do you remember the young man who worked with the ice man? How important we thought he was. This young man with the bulging muscles would push open the door with his foot, walk in speedily so as not to drip water on the floor and maneuver the ice into the ice box with expert skill. One time when Mama got through baking and offered him a piece of honey cake he was so gracious he let her in on a trade secret: "If you put a piece of burlap around the ice and pour salt over the ice, it will last twice as long," he explained confidentially.

Oh, were we thrilled. A real trade secret nobody else knew. And it never would have happened unless Mama gave him the cake. Oh, how we guarded that secret - until we found all the neighbors were doing the same thing for years.

I wonder how many remember the man who came around with a little pony and a camera to take pictures of kids on his horse? Oh boy, did we think he was important! The only other person we knew who owned a horse was Tom Mix. How we marveled at this man's great knowledge; when he would put his hand inside the camera, stir something, and in a matter of minutes extract a picture. Of course the pictures would crack and fade in less than a week - but, we were certain he was a man of great importance.

And who doesn't remember the Bungalow Bar man with his beautiful white truck built like a miniature bungalow? Oh, how we envied his children. We were certain they never had to pay for ice cream - after all, we figured - what father would charge his own children for ice cream?

And even in school, how we envied the older boys in the upper grades. They would always be called by the principal to carry books someplace. What authority, what status, to walk into the principal's office without an official summons!

In the classroom we envied the monitors. Remember the bathroom monitor? This was a kid the teacher would always send out to the bathroom if a youngster left the room for too long a period. He would inspect the 'boys' bathroom and if he found you just standing there he would "turn you in." Oh, how important this kid was. We thought he had the power of life and death! I'll never forget the time this kid was sick and the teacher made me a substitute bathroom monitor. I never got over it! It was the closest I'd ever get to being elected President of the United States, I thought. When the kid came back the next day - I prayed all term long that he should get sick. After all, I was his understudy! After I became his substitute he would confide in me and say - if he ever caught me in the bathroom - he wouldn't turn me in

– because I was one of the elite!

I'll never forget the matrons in the movies who were supposed to look after the children. I don't know where they got them, but they were always fat and mean-looking. Heaven help you if a matron ever caught you sitting any place except in the children's section. If this ever happened – it meant the firing squad – we were certain!

As we grew older, sometimes we would sneak away from the children's section and sit in the adult section. But we never enjoyed the movie – because we watched the screen with one eye and the other was always on the matron! If she caught us, she would lean over gently with her flashlight – this alone was authority – and softly whisper, "Are you here with your parents?"

And we, like little dopes, would nod "no!" Then she would stiffen up, shine the light in our faces and snap, "COME WITH ME!"

We were positive it meant certain death! But we were always stuck back in the children's section with the reprimand, "If you pull that again – I'll call the manager!" *Gut vais* (heaven knows) – what would happen then! *Oy*, was she important! Then, one day, we found out she was some kid's mother who went to our school, and did we look at him with awe. We were certain his mother always let him sit in the adult section –after all, she was the *mashgiach* (overseer) of the movie!

And do you remember the kid the teacher selected to pull the stage curtain in the auditorium during assembly programs? Did we envy this kid! It was up to him whether the curtain opened for the screen and we saw the show or not. I'll never forget coming home with a kid who opened the curtain one day in the assembly. I introduced him to Mama with such great pride. He told me what was behind the curtain and I hung on every word. Oh, was this kid important, I thought!

And how about the kid who has a mother who taught in the same school! *Oy*, was this kid important! We did everything but bow down before him to win his approval. We would see him wait for his mother at the teachers' entrance and then get in a car with his mother and our own teacher! That was importance! And whenever a test was given (he never failed), we were certain his mother got the answers from our teacher the day before! But my stock went up one day when my cousin Lily, who was a substitute teacher, taught in my school. Oh, did I use that for stature. When I passed her in the hall I was bursting with pride and was all set to call out, "Hi Lily!" just too show how well I knew her – but when the moment came all I could do was nod – and smile – and the kids thought I was fooling. They didn't believe she was really my cousin. To prove she was, I waited in front of the teachers' entrance that day, but she had left by a different exit and I had to wait a whole year before she subbed in my school again.

And when I went to good old Evander Childs High School on Gun Hill Road, Lily's husband, Willie Weinstein, was the gym teacher. Just think, my cousin in charge of the whole gym! What excitement!

One day when I forgot my sneakers he called me out of the line. My heart pounded. My own cousin! He couldn't be turning me in! After all, what did I do that was so wrong? As I came up to him he smiled and asked, "How's the folks?"

"Fine," I swallowed hard.

"Everything all right in school?" he questioned, and I think some of the kids even heard that... *Oy*, did I beam! Was I important. After all, how many kids had cousins who were their own gym teachers?

But it worked in reverse – from me he expected more!

And who doesn't remember the trolley car conductor – motorman. When we went to school, who knew from busses? Somehow or other we always got the most crotchety driver in the system. If the kids would clown around in the car he would stop the trolley, no matter where he was and shout, "If you don't sit down I'll throw you off my car!" What authority!

I'll never forget one of the kids in the neighborhood who worked Saturday nights in the candy store making sodas. If you were a friend he would even give you the extra bottle caps from sodas with which we made checkers. What importance to work behind the counter and put in as much syrup as he wanted - for friends!

And how important we thought the man who worked behind the delicatessen counter was. He could take a piece of salami any time he wanted without paying for it. And it was up to him whether you got an 'extra' mustard in an order, or an extra string of sauerkraut when you bought a hot dog! *Oy* was this guy important! He was always grumpy. When some kids came in and bought merchandise and asked for an extra mustard package he would cut them down with, "Mustard costs money –you got money?" What could we answer? He had the authority!

And in shul on the High Holy Days - how we trembled at the man who always slammed his hand down on a book shouting, "Sha - Sha!" *Oy*, was he important, we thought! He could bang on a book and make more noise than we - and the Rabbi didn't say a word to him. And the man who always had the same seat next to the window - how important he was. On hot simmering days - even the Rabbi would have to plead with him to open the window. There were times sweat poured down his brow but he wouldn't open the window. That was authority!

Yes sir, we knew important people in our youth. And even today, people we know with comparatively ordinary jobs are still so important. For example, when you go rowing in the park and are only supposed to row for one hour and when you come back it's a minute past the hour - the kid who checks the card suddenly takes on such great importance - is he or is he not going to charge you for the other hour? And it's the same in parking lots. The man who checks your parking ticket to compute how long you stayed - you stand like a dope hoping he gives you the benefit of the fraction of a minute.

But why go on? There are so many important people in this world!

THE BEST ON THE BLOCK

We had specialists even in those days, and some of those kids had unusual specialties.

WE HAD ONE JERKY KID IN OUR NEIGHBORhood, Moishe Sunshine. He had a specialty and used to pick up what we thought was a small fortune, climbing down the sewers to retrieve balls that rolled into the sewers over the course of a few days. Sometimes Moishe used to haul up between five and ten balls a day. Sometimes, he would hit a bonanza with three or four 'Spaldines' in his harvest. The truth was, he always smelled like a sewer – this kid never got close enough to water to wash off that smell. But, he was good for fifteen to twenty cents a day – climbing down sewers. He sold the balls "wholesale" because they were secondhand.

We had another kid on our block who could imitate a police siren so perfectly you would swear a police car was in front of you. When Lester Pearlman took a deep breath and let go - people used to open their windows to see why a police car was stopping in front of the house. In school, Lester was left back almost every year -even though he was a nice guy. He and school never got along. But he could make the sound of a police siren so real that it was unbelievable.

We also had the distinct honor of having the best "stoop jumper" in the entire neighborhood living in our house. Howie Firestein could jump twelve steps on the front stoop and land on his feet with such grace - it was a pleasure watching him. Of course, when we would have the yearly competition we always managed to wind up with a few twisted ankles before the day would end. But Howie could jump further and swifter than any other kid on the block! Howie had one other notable distinction going for him, too: in the labyrinth hollowness of the hallway, Howie could bring on a *grepse*, (a belch) at will, that would shatter your eardrums! People would open their doors to see what exploded - then of course we would run away. No one really ever knew who the phantom *grepser* was, but now you know.

We had one girl on the block, Muriel Gradowitz, who used to take singing lessons and *a gantza tug* (a whole day) she would be *kvitchering* - something about "Hark now - hear the angels...tra-la-la-la..." and *azoy hut zee gemacht a gantza tug!* (That's how she sang a whole day). Funny thing about it - she had a pretty good voice -but in the heat of the summer, with everybody's window open - who wanted to hear for three hours, "Hark now hear the angels - tra-la-la...!"

On our block we always had one kid who was the "ice cream announcer." This kid, Seymour Moscowitz, would stand on the corner and with his radar-like ears would listen for the tingle of the ice cream truck bell that was blocks away and shout, "The ice cream man is coming!" He would run up the block like a nut to get ice cream money and like Paul Revere shout, "The ice cream man is coming! The ice cream man is coming!"

Oy, did we have characters on our block. Every kid had some specialty that separated him from the rest. For example, Bobby Silver was the best hopscotch player on our block. With a broken ankle, Bobby played out a whole game and won. Of course, we had to carry him home and then to the hospital – but he stuck with it!

We had another dopey kid who used to be able to twist his lips in such a fashion that you would swear his teeth were coming out. This was Herbert Freedman. A handsome kid he wasn't, but when he would force his lip into those crazy positions and stand in line at the bakery – they always gave him immediate service. They figured he was having an attack!

We had one girl on our block who everybody said was *ah bumiker*! (a tramp). Why? Because it was rumored she wore nail polish and sometimes, people said, they saw her with lipstick! The truth was she never used lipstick – but, would chew on a red beet before she went out to a party – that gave the same effect! Those lips were so red – we thought she simply had 'ah condition'!

We had Sammy Goldstein who lived on our block and it was rumored that Sammy was 'ah bum' because Sammy never worked. He always hung around the house. His mother used to yell on him all the time, "Sammy, *du fa curst meir der yoren* – you are shortening my life – go out and get a job!"

She would sigh to Mama, "*Ut voxt ah bum*. (Here grows a bum.)"

Mama would try to console her and point out that Sammy was simply a thinker and when the right job came along he would know it!

It finally did – Sammy got himself a job as a runner for a Wall Street firm, and after a few years he was able to buy and sell the whole neighborhood!

We lived in a neighborhood that was really a cross - section of today's world. From our block came doctors, lawyers and a number of fine educators. We also had our share of bookmakers and some skullduggerous characters I prefer to forget, but they also helped hone the edge of wit and understanding that became part of our character. In one case, one of the kids on the block became a cop and another the fugitive that the cop had to go out and catch. And the attorney who represented the hood also came from our block. And the judge who sentenced the hood was first cousin to the family who lived on our ground floor.

I'll never forget the girl in the building across the way from us who was an artist. If I remember correctly she was kind of a strange girl - always carrying canvas and sticks into her house, wearing a dark blue skirt that was always covered with paint smears. The neighbors called her 'ah shlumper' (a slob) - but she was a very nice girl. Then one day we learned that she won a prize for one of her paintings. Right away our druggist emptied his store window and put in about a dozen of Selma Gautbaum's artistic creations. It was something to see. Nobody understood her work - it was surrealistic - you know the kind with straight lines and smears in different directions. But that was Selma's claim to fame. Her paintings hung next to the Dr. Scholl's foot pads, and hernia apparatus! Let me ask you - what is fame? Who says you have to hang in a museum?

The following week she hung more pictures in our fruit store. Nobody really understood her work - but they all had fancy titles like, "Colliding Worlds," and "A Mother's Prayer," and I'll never forget this one, "The Clothesline." That picture was pure white canvas with a gray smear running through the middle. Nothing else! Our fruit man bought that one for five dollars and kept it hanging in the fruit store to add to the store's decor for years. However, the painting improved over the years because from time to time crushed plums would spatter onto the pure white canvas and sometimes some oranges would rub against it and the new color blends made it even more exciting. Before Teppelman closed the fruit store it was rumored that he sold the painting for ten dollars - making 100% profit! The fruit smears gave the picture character!

Whatever happened to Selma - *vere vais?* (Who knows?) The last I heard she got married, had a family and now draws pictures for her children!

I guess every block was a world unto itself. There was always love, and hate, happiness and tragedy. But somehow, we always stood together - we didn't nitpick. We were all part of the same block-world that gave us the basic training to survive in today's world!

A SUIT GROWS
ON STANTON STREET

Unless you went shopping for a suit on Stanton Street in New York City before the High Holy Days – you missed a great part of yesterday's world.

IT WAS THE SAME EVERY YEAR. JUST ABOUT three weeks before the High Holy Days, Mama would assemble the brood, have us put on what was considered our new clothing to see if we wouldn't disgrace our tribe on the High Holy Days. After all, we couldn't look like *shlumpers*. (slobs).

It was always the same – my little brother Berel's pants had gaping holes in the knees. This meant a new suit!

There were hundreds of clothing stores in our neighborhood – but for Mama and Papa – Stanton Street on the Lower East Side was the only place where we would buy a suit.

Let me tell you something, you had to know how to buy on Stanton Street! It was a must that you had to take along a *maivin*.(an expert). This *maivin* was supposed to know goods, style, fit and most important of all – some salesman who would cut the price to the bone!

My uncle Louie was considered the "Suit *maivin*." Papa was the "coat *maivin*" and an aunt was the "Dress *maivin*!" And I want you to know – never did they interfere with each others' maivin-ing.

Nu – so Uncle Louie was called to be the *maivin* for a suit for Berel.

How he ever became a suit Maivin we could never understand because he worked in a fruit store! But who were we to ask questions?

We took the train downtown to Stanton Street. We went to Lieberman and Rind, a store in which Uncle Louie had told us the salesman was an old friend and would give us a suit for less than wholesale cost.

He knowingly explained, "Irving grew up with me in Europe. He's such a good salesman that when I come in he tells the *balaboss* (boss) I'm a relative. You see, the sales help get the suits for cost."

When we walked into the store we were greeted by a chubby smiling little man who clutched Uncle Louie's hand warmly and greeted him by turning toward the back of the store, shouting, "Chaim, (Chaim was their tailor) look who's here."

What a greeting! The tailor came out and clutched Uncle Louie's hand warmly, "We just got in suits – like gold! Wait! Hershel," he called out, "Bring out the suit I told you to put away for my grandson."

Hershel disappeared into the back of the store and then came out with a suit. It was the most horrible color green you ever saw. He held up the jacket and beamed, "Is dot ah suit – or is dot ah suit? Here, feel the *varer*, (material) like silk!"

Mama raised her eyebrows and said, "I don't like the color. *Vee kumpts ah greener suit for a kindt?*" (How do you show a green suit for a child).

The salesman was wounded. He turned to Mama and exclaimed, "Would I sell you *ah* suit like this for the child? I only want to see the size and the fit. Come, put on the jacket - I want to see the size."

He grabbed Berel by the nape of his neck and let him slip into the jacket. To start with, Berel looked like a blimp - but in that green stripe suit - *oy - kenst brechen!* (You could have thrown up.)

"Stand," the salesman snapped as Berel began to squirm. "Stand, sonny boy, and look in the mirror. Stand!" he ordered. Then he stood back admiringly and exclaimed, "*Az ah yahr auf mir - vee shain!*" (I should live for another year how nice that looks.)

Mama shrugged, "But I don't like the color."

The salesman then turned to Uncle Louie - our *maivin* - and softly questioned, "What do you say Louie - is dot ah fit?"

Uncle Louie went over and tugged at the jacket in the back, then the sides, then at the neck. He stood back like an artist admiring and questioning a piece of art. Then he said, "*Takeh* - the color is nice but the collar doesn't lay so good. See if you have another one, maybe in blue?"

The salesman was wounded once more - but the *maivin* had spoken!

In a few minutes he returned with a dark blue suit.

"Louie, I just took this off the rack, the boss put this away for his son. Quick, have the child put it on before he comes back."

Uncle Louie quickly assisted the salesman as both tried to fit the jacket on Berel. It was sort of like fitting a tent! Berel was no lightweight when he was a kid.

Both men tugged at the suit as Berel kept squirming.

"Stand," ordered the salesman, "Stand!"

"I can't, it itches!" Berel replied.

The salesman stepped back with a warm smile, "Is dot ah suit - like it was made for him! Dot material is imported worsted!"

We didn't know what it meant but figured it had to be good or else he wouldn't have made such an issue of it!

"How's dot for ah color? Navy blue with a touch of blue serge stripe! Dot's ah banker's suit!" Then he leaned over to Mama and whispered, "Listen, if you like it let me take it off the child before my boss comes back from lunch. He put this suit away for his own son!"

Mama looked at Papa, and Papa looked at Uncle Louie for a sign. Uncle Louie stepped forward, grabbed the collar, tugged at the seat, and pulled at the lapels. "*Takeh - ah* perfect fit!"

Uncle Louie leaned over to the salesman and asked, "*Nu - vee fil far dem suit?*" (How much for the suit?)

The salesman smiled warmly, "Listen, Louie, for you I'm giving it away, twenty-five dollars, but you must do the alterations!"

Mama and Papa shook their heads. Louie turned to the salesman and snapped, "Me you ask twenty-five dollars - like I'm off the street?"

The salesman held his hands in a prayer-like fashion and looked upwards. "I should see on my own children as many good years as more than twenty-five dollars we're getting for this suit. But, listen, I'll give up my commission; OK, twenty dollars. Let me wrap it up."

Uncle Louie looked at him and snapped, "You want to lose me as a friend? Twenty dollars for this piece of garbage? To tell the truth, I wouldn't let the child wear ah suit like dot in shul. You saw how it fit, like a rag! Not a cent more than fifteen dollars."

The salesman practically began to cry. "I swear on my wife's grave that this suit cost Moe nineteen dollars. I saw the bill when it came in."

"Not a penny more than sixteen will I give you," Louie snapped indignantly.

"Listen – I'll have to put it back on the rack. As it is I'm risking my job to sell you dot suit. Moe was going to charge his own brother twenty dollars for dot suit."

Uncle Louie threw the jacket to the counter and snapped, "If that's what you think of me you can keep it. Dot suit isn't worth a nickel more than seventeen dollars."

"Make it seventeen-fifty," the salesman pleaded.

Mama nodded and the salesman, quickly grabbed the jacket and pants and put them in a box, with a broad smile on his face. "It's such a pleasure to do business with you." Then he turned to Louie and exclaimed, "Listen, why don't you stop in more often – it's such a pleasure to talk with you. My wife sends her regards. *Sei mir gezunt!*" (You should be healthy).

He handed Mama the package and Papa paid him.

When we got home, Papa first had to make the cuffs, adjust the jacket and take in the pants. It was a beautiful suit, but it really didn't matter much because so few people paid attention to it – the hole in the knees of his pants Berel got two minutes after putting it on always distracted them!

WHEN A BAR MITZVAH WAS A BAR MITZVAH

Remember when an invitation to a catered Bar Mitzvah was a big thing? The family planned for the event for months.

ODAY, WHEN YOU GET A BAR MITZVAH invitation, the modern American has to see if it will fit in with the family social calendar. And heaven forbid if there's a conflict, *gevald!*

In our day whenever an invitation was sent out it always said, "...and family." This meant the whole tribe was primed for the zero hour. It wasn't a show-off type of affair. We felt wanted.

Today, when you get an invitation it's usually only for the adults — the only kids they invite are the little monsters the Bar Mitzvah boy fights with all year round.

In our day when they invited kids to a Bar Mitzvah, the

little cousins all sat at a "children's table" and that was that. Today, they put all the little monsters at a "main table" in the front of the hall and everybody *kvells* (beams) at their antics. In truth they look like a miniature version of Murder Incorporated. A haircut — these kids never heard of it! They look like a bunch of sheep dogs let out to pasture. That's a style?

When we were kids we looked forward to meeting an uncle or an aunt we hadn't seen for some time. Today's kids wouldn't be found dead being introduced to their relatives - in fact, they're ashamed to be associated with their parents. Honest! Did you ever see them when they enter a hall with the family? They walk ahead like they're part of somebody else's.

To us a Bar Mitzvah reception was a time we said hello to our relatives then proceeded to slide all over the neatly polished dance floor. That was fun! When we got tired of sliding we would stand in front of the musicians and watch the trumpet player's eyes bulge as he played a *frailach*.

And listen — in those days we had musicians. Today, if Con Edison ever went on strike on the night of your affair, you're out of luck. Did you ever see today's klesmers? One has an electric guitar with an electric amplifier, another an electric accordian that sounds like an organ in a church, another with an electric xylophone, and another *noch shlepper* with an electric drum. If the microphone breaks down you can't hear the singer. If a fuse blows you can't hear the band. And sometimes this is a blessing!

And the music they play — you think they know the old time music that used to really make an affair — a *nechtiger tug*! (forget it!) To them three choruses of "Fiddler on the Roof" is Yiddish music! Have you gone to an affair lately? That's all they play! For an encore they play "Matchmaker, Matchmaker." Whatever happened to *Shain vi di Lovoneh, or Aishes Chayil, or Mine Shteteleh Belz*?

And even the waiters they have today are different. Remember when we were kids — the most ill-tempered waiter in the house always got the children's table. This guy was just miserable — he put the food down like he wished we'd choke on it. You see, in those days you had to tip the waiters and whoever got the children's table, naturally got no tip. Would you be happy?

I'll never forget one affair we went to. My cousin Melvin was some character. Whenever he wanted something — he would threaten his mother and father with, "I'll f'wo up..."

And Melvin could do this on cue. Whenever he went to an affair and they put him at the children's table he would cry. "I wanna sit at Papa's table — with the big people...or else I'll f'wo up!" He'd pause, then add, "in uncle Louie's pocket."

But after all, the relatives invited Melvin with the idea that he would sit at the children's table — where they paid half price for the dinner. If he sat at the grown-up people's table, they would be billed for another adult. *Nu, nu* — need I tell you what went on at every affair?

But Melvin had a secret weapon — when he did stay at the children's table — he could mix up a concoction that no chemist in this world could match.

No matter what they put on the table, Melvin would mix this in a glass and tell the other kids it was an ancient Hebrew herb mixture — very good for sore throats!

One of his mixtures would begin when they served the fruit cocktail. Melvin would take the juice from the cup and put that into the glass. So far, so good. Then he would add a good helping of salt and pepper, mix in some plain soda and watch the salt and soda begin to form a mushroom-shaped cloud. Then he would take a little *chrein* (horseradish) that they served with the gefilte fish. He would then crush in a few of the cookies that were always on the table, add a little ginger ale, and then some after dinner mints to finish the cocktail.

He would smack his lips together telling us it was a delightful drink. He would let my little brother Berel be the first to sip this concoction. Berel took one sip and promptly "f'wew up." In less than ten minutes all the kids at the table were burping all over the place. The only one who wasn't was Melvin — he didn't need any drink — he could do it on cue.

That was some Melvin!

And another thing. In our day who knew from "candids" at a Bar Mitzvah? Today, not only do they take pictures, they also take television pictures. And from the second the photographer turns on his sun lamp everybody makes believe they're in Hollywood. And like idiots everybody waves at the camera.

And then weeks after the affair when you visit the Bar Mitzvah boy's family you sit for hours looking at the still picture album and then the movies or T.V. and then you sit and look at the color slides. And everybody says "Oooo— ahhh." At the affair nobody was talking to the host or hostess because they put them at a table with relatives who they don't talk with. All of a sudden "...it was some affair — *ain klainikite!*"

But in our day when the affair was over that was it. We simply looked forward to the next. Of course, a discussion of "who gave what" always followed. Those were the days that people gave gold pieces—remember?

But let's face it. Today's world has many advantages. After all, in those days who would think of serving "ice cream" (you know the kind that 's not made from milk) after a meat meal? And today the big conversation when it's served is, "Isn't it amazing, it tastes just like real ice cream...!"

But the old timers still stick to their guns — they don't trust it!

Yes sir, it's a new world.

MUSTARD PLASTERS
AND YARTZEIT GLASSES

How come we weren't concerned with ecology in our day? It's simple - we had nothing to throw out to louse up the environment! In those years what went to waste?

TODAY EVERYBODY STILL TALKS ABOUT OUR environment - and rightfully so. Here, let me give you ah f'rinstance! In those years when Mama went to the grocery store to buy cheese, the pimento cheese we loved came in little glasses with beautiful designs on the side. If you ate enough pimento cheese - you wound up with a gorgeous set of juice glasses!

Drinking glasses were another thing. In all honesty, I didn't know what a real drinking glass was until I got married. We always drank out of used *yartzeit* (memorial) glasses. This was how we thought it was supposed to be.

Every glass weighed a ton! Who was to tell us different? A glass was a glass!

Today, who saves burned out *yartzeit* glasses? I still have the set of glasses Mama gave us when I got married. It was a mixed set of juice and water glasses. Just plain pimento cheese and *yartzeit* glasses!

Years ago when you bought tea, tea was tea! Who knew from tea bags? It came in a little metal box that looked like a pirate's treasure chest. Remember the "Swee-Touch-Nee" tea boxes? Those little boxes served a million and one purposes in the house. Who would ever dare to throw one out? They were used to keep buttons, needles, thread, nuts and bolts, stamps, everything! For years I thought that's why Mama bought those boxes. Was I surprised when I found out they were originally used to hold tea!

Let me ask you, remember when you needed a bottle opener to open a bottle of soda? Today, everything is with the twist- off cap - and if you have a little arthritis in the fingers - *takeh* you're in trouble! The pull-top cans (I am certain were designed by the band-aid manufacturers) have even replaced the automatic can openers! See - *ut* is automation becoming obsolete!

The new look has even reached the boxes of chocolate candy we once enjoyed. Remember when chocolate candies came with those little pleated pieces of chocolate brown paper? Each chocolate had its own little piece of paper. In fact, when we were kids and Mama wouldn't give us a second piece of chocolate, we would munch on the little papers, they looked and smelled so good!

Today the boxes of chocolate candy come with one little plastic receptacle for all the candies. Feh! Years ago, the Whitman miniature chocolates used to even come in a pretty purple metal box that also served a million and one uses. Who didn't save one of those boxes to keep special bills or letters or stamps in? In fact, our office still uses one of those little Whitman chocolate candy boxes to hold the office stamps.

Once upon a time when you opened a box of candy they had a little diagram on the cover that showed you where the nuts were, or where the fruits were. Today, the diagrams are gone – replaced by a design, that we need like a *loch in kup*, (hole in the head) and it's Russian roulette every time you take a piece of candy. If you like fruits you always get a nut.

Everything in today's world has changed. Remember when people used to keep gloves in the glove compartment of a car? Today, you can stop a thousand cars and never find a single glove in one of those compartments.

Don't laugh, we had a form of automation even in our years. When Mama put out a wet mop on the fire escape, and water dripped down, she was watering Mrs. Mermelstein's plants that were all over her fire escape on the floor below. *Shoen!* Automation!

In our world, who ever saw garbage in the streets? First of all, who had garbage? We ate everything or Mama would split our head! It was "*Ess und brech*"! (Eat till you burst). And what we couldn't eat we planted! Who bought plants in those years? We saved the orange and lemon pits and planted them in the little wooden cheese boxes we got from the grocery store. Remember those cheese boxes? They produced the most beautiful little plants you might want to see. If we wanted real greenery, Mama would take a sweet potato and place it in a *yartzeit* glass of water and in a few weeks we had the most beautiful plant money could buy.

If it wasn't the sweet potato season, we could always find an onion that was beginning to sprout stalks among Mama's onions. This we would put in a juice glass filled with water and – shoen – we had greenery! Of course, it smelled like hell – but listen – who cared? We were improving the ecology.

We lived in a period of time that was simple and uncomplicated. All our parents expected of us was a little respect.

What delicacies did we have in those years? We were very unsophisticated in our food tastes. We took the end crust of a piece of pumpernickel, rubbed it well with a clove of garlic, then sprinkled it liberally with salt and *shoen* we had supper! *Vus hut gefelt?* – what was missing? *Ut* was a *mychel*! It was tasty, filling and nutritious. Besides, no one came near you for a week!

In those years, who had money for fancy things that came in plastic bags? You were lucky if you got a paper bag in some stores! Whoever heard of the word **poverty**? We didn't even know we were poor – *vus hut uns gefelt*? What was missing to us? If we were hungry, a piece of bread and butter was a meal! – Or for a *fleishica*, a meat meal – a little chicken shmaltz on a thick slice of pumpernickel sprinkled with salt – *ut* was a meal!

Mama and Papa were much too busy raising a family to realize we were poor. We had things that money couldn't buy – like bills!

When we got sick – who called a doctor? Who knew from Blue Cross? A half dozen neighbors would hold a medical conference – decide all that was needed was a little mustard plaster on the chest to burn out the illness and – *shoen* we were cured. Those mustard plasters cured everything from hang nail to athlete's foot! When they put those mustard plasters on – *gevald*! – If you survived the plaster – the cold became secondary. The truth was the mustard plaster caused such discomfort – suffering with a cold became a pleasure!

But today's world is different. Today some of the kids wear long hair and beards. The truth is these kids have an insight we never really had. The ones with long hair can wear a shirt with a frayed collar for months without anybody even guessing because you cannot even see their neck. And if some of the kids grow their beards any longer they wouldn't have to wear sweaters!

So you see, it's *takeh* a new world!

WHO NEEDED HOMEWORK?

When we were kids we felt homework was the most inhumane form of torture developed by man. We were certain it was created by a generation whose purpose it was to destroy us.

I WILL NEVER FORGET HOW MY LITTLE brother Berel's homework book was always a disaster zone! After he copied down in his little assignment book what he assumed the teacher had written on the blackboard, he was never certain of what he wrote. He couldn't read his own handwriting. When he would call any of his classmates to find out what the assignment was, no matter who he called – each kid had something else! If he would check with three kids he wound up with three different homeworks!

The teacher wrote the homework on the blackboard in good faith, and the kids would copy it down in good faith.

But what happened to the homework assignment in the process of copying it from the blackboard to their assignment book – *Gevald*!

You have to say one thing for my little brother Berel, he was innovative when it came to homework. I remember the time he had a little friend over. The two of them were supposed to do their homework together! Right away we knew this was a mistake when they discovered each had a different set of numbers for examples they copied off the board! They did their arithmetic like a President negotiating his budget with Congress. No matter what answer one came up with the other kept saying, "Too much...too much!"

Then there was a period of collective bargaining.

"I'll give you the answer to number three if you give me the answer to number five," one would suggest, as the other countered with, " I'll give you the answer to number five if you give me the answers to number one and number two, because number five is twice as hard as number three! *Shoen*!

Let me tell you something, when we were kids, doing homework with a friend was rare. "Homework is to be done in your home," Mama would shout when we would suggest going to a friend's house to do homework.

My little brother occasionally did his homework in school.

"How come you don't have homework?" Mama would question Berel when he came home.

"I did it in school," he would shrug.

"So it's not homework – it's schoolwork! Where will you do the schoolwork? At home?" she pressed.

When Mama opened his book, it looked like he had done the homework while sitting in a roller coaster! *Gevald*! Did that kid have a handwriting! Adding insult to injury he used to write it in ink with a broken, scratchy pen. If he made a mistake he would put a little spit on his finger and rub the page until it either wore through to the other side or made an indistinguishable "shmear"!

I want you to know this kid was so sure of himself, that even when he got a simple arithmetic example wrong, he would try to convince the teacher that even in industry there was a margin for minimal error. "Look, I was only off by one - I'm not a C.P.A.!" he'd argue.

And there were times his teachers stopped to think *takeh*, what was so *geferlach* if two and two equalled five? When he came to four and four he'd make it seven! *Shoen!* So what was so bad? It balanced out.

When it came to spelling, let me tell you something, he was a real winner. Once he got passed "cat" and "dog" - he was in trouble. I'll never forget the time he had to take a spelling test and was given the word 'committee.' He spelled it 'comite.' When the teacher marked it wrong he went up to complain - "I was writing about a small 'committee'! If you wanted a big 'committee' I would have doubled up on the letters." So she gave him 100% for salesmanship and zero for spelling!

I'll never forget the time Berel had to produce his very first book report! *Oy*, was that an ordeal! First of all, Berel was allergic to books. Every time he would pick one up he'd break out in a rash. In those days who put pictures in books? Books had words. You had to read! Occasionally, there would be a picture but it was so far into the book who could tell what the book was about just from the one or two pictures?

When my sisters were young, Mama had gotten a set of the "Bobbsey Twins" books from a neighbor whose daughter had outgrown them. My sisters loved to read them. Nu, so when it came time for Berel to read a book - Mama gave him the Bobbsey Twins. Let's face it - a book's a book!

He scanned the book all of two minutes then said he was ready to write his book report!

"Dope," we shouted, "ya have to read the book first!"

"I did," he shouted back.

"Oh yeah," my sisters would taunt - "What's it about?"

"The Bobbsey Twins," he would whine.

"What did they do?" they'd ask.

"I don't have to know that!" he shouted, then he'd scream to Mama in the kitchen, "Ma - they're yelling on me and I can't do my homework."

"How could you write a book report if you didn't read the book," Mama would question. "How are you going to tell the teacher what the book is about, Tateleh," Mama soothed.

He thought for a minute and turned to my sister. "What's the book about - I already know its name and who wrote it. You don't have to tell me that part!"

"Read it yourself!" she would snap as she did her own homework.

"Ma-a-a," he'd whine - "see, she's starting up!"

Mama would urge him to read at least two pages and then maybe my sisters would tell him the rest. He'd sit down and start reading. After thirty-two seconds he'd look up and exclaim, "I finished! - What's the book about?"

"First tell me what the first two pages are about," my sister would demand.

"The Bobbsey Twins," he'd reply confidently.

"Yeah - but what are they doing?" she asked.

"Ma-a-a, she's starting up!" he'd scream.

After a series of incursions of this nature, a battle royal would take place. Then he sat down to write the report.

In a big blurry scrawl he wrote, "The Bobbsey Twins," and then the author's name. Underneath that he wrote, "This book is about the Bobbsey twins. I liked this book very much!"

Shoen! Book report!

When he got to school the next day, by sheer coincidence, one of his classmates had done a report on the same Bobbsey Twins book. The teacher asked that child to read her report. The kid did a fantastic job, capturing every detail of the book. Then the teacher called on Berel to read his report. The little dope got up, looked as his paper with the one sentence written on it, and ad-libbed the entire report based on what the little girl had previously read. Naturally, he got an A for the recitation. But, when the teacher asked him to turn in his report, he almost died. As he walked hesitantly toward her desk with the one sentence report, he tripped over Sarah Benimowitz's briefcase and accidentally splattered the whole paper with the bottle of Waterman's ink she had on her desk.

"What a pity," Mrs. Gordon sighed, "but you can copy it over this evening at home."

The little dope went home and wrote a report that his teacher was so proud of, she sent it around to all the teachers and even the principal, as a example of what it means for a child to read a book!

Nu – I ask you...?

WHEN A LITVAK
MARRIED A GALITZIANA

Today every culture is concerned with intermarriage, assimilation and integration, and it was so in our years, only then when a Litvak married a Galitziana that was considered an intermarriage! Both families would cry.

INTEGRATION FOR US IS NOTHING NEW! WE were integrated when we were kids - in some classes they mixed in kids who had Litvak parents with others who had Galitziana parents! And I want you to know, the feud that history records about "the Hatfields and the McCoys" was nothing compared to the feuds that existed between Litvaks and Galitzianas.

Listening to the folks talk, we always thought pretty women were Galitzianas! If a woman had a fiery temper - we were always led to believe "*ut* is *ah Galitziana.*" Or if a neighbor's kid had the freedom of the street and would run around like a nut, the neighbors would whisper, "*Vus vais a kiend fun Galitz*? (What does a child from Galitz know?)

I want you to know we were so brainwashed we were led to believe you could always tell "Galitzianisher cooking" especially when they put sugar and cinnamon on blintzes! Litvaks always used pepper and salt!

We were led to believe that Galitzianas put salt on grapefruit, while Litvaks used sugar! Listen – who were we to question?

Everything we bought in those years was relative – relative to a Jewish holiday or a cousin's Bar Mitzvah – or even a wedding. If we needed a new pair of shoes – Mama would always say, "Wait, wait, when the Jewish holidays come you'll get," or "Wait, wait cousin Lilly's wedding is coming, then you'll get shoes."

My little brother Berel would whine, "But Ma, my feet are showing through the bottom!"

Mama would snap back with, "Walk on your heels and put in another piece of cardboard till Lilly's wedding. What do you want – to go to the wedding like ah shlump?"

You know, I just realized that many of the younger generation are probably scratching their heads wondering what this bit about Galitzianas and Litvaks is really all about! The Litvaks came from Latvia or Russia and the Galitzianas came from around Galitzia or the Balkans. They were all Jews, but Jews with different temperaments. The majority of those we always thought were Galitzianas were usually very pretty women. A Litvak woman, the very few we were able to identify, were wholesome but not as pretty as a real Galitziana!

I'll never forget the time my little brother came home from school with one of those "true confession" type magazines that had pictures of very pretty ladies, not necessarily dressed like a Rebbetzin! When Mama found the book under Berel's pillow she exploded. You know what his retort was? "Ma-a-a-a, I only brought the book home to show you Galitzianas!" He got a shot in the mouth and *shoen* - the demonstration was over!

I'll never forget the time my uncle married a very sweet young lady who happened to be a Galitziana - like I said, that was an intermarriage! Well, that sweet little lady turned out to be one of the biggest Litvak-bigots you ever saw. Boy, could she throw a dig or ah *shnide* - like a *shochet*. (one who slaughters cattle). If during one of the family get-togethers someone would talk about a cousin who was failing in business, this Galitziana aunt would cut in with "*Nu - vus vais a Litvak?*" (What does a Litvak know?)

There would be a few choice words tossed around, punctuated in harsh tones, "*Zull zee brenen - de fabrenter Galitz*" (May she burn, the burning Galitz).

But, by the next family get-together all was forgotten! Of course, when everybody sat down - the Litvaks sat on one side of the room and the Galitzianas sat on the other - with each side glaring at one another!

So even though we were brainwashed in our formative years to the dangers of intermarriage with Galitzianas - Mama and Papa lost the battle - we all married Galitzianas! And you know what we discovered, Galitzianas really don't put sugar and cinnamon on blintzes - at least my wife doesn't! She buys them that way from the grocery! I also discovered that Galitzianas don't necessarily put salt on grapefruit - my little Galitz puts salt on everything. Don't believe it when they say 'revenge is sweet.' It isn't - it's salty!

And after forty-one years of being married to a Galitz, I also learned that Galitzianas don't have fiery tempers - they just throw things!

Let me tell you something - there is nothing as vengeful as a Galitziana. Whenever I have a fight with my wife - she becomes quiet and never argues back. She strikes back in her own way. She doesn't rinse the soap out of my underwear. Listen - you think it's funny! It's the truth!

Let me tell you something - I'm as open-minded as the next one - but we were always told that Litvaks had the brains. And as the years pass I begin to believe it more and more.

But why talk - to each his own. Here, you wanna see how perceptive we were when we were kids - I never heard a Litvak uncle or aunt able to pronounce the letter 's' in a sentence. It always came out as 'sh.' The 's' was always *funfert* (blurred) with the 'sh' sound. *Nu*, so our Rebbe was a Litvak. Whenever he would shout "Sit down!" the 's' always took on the 'sh' sound and we would go into hysterics!

And the Galitzianas always spoke a little funny too - they could never pronounce the 'aye' sound. It always came out as an 'I' sound. Like try to say, "*Ich gay a'haim.*" (I go home) That always came out as, "*Ich guy a haim!*" It was sort of Bostonian Yiddish!

Despite the notorious tempers Galitzianas were supposed to have, Litvaks were equally noted for their stubbornness. *Gevald,* when a Litvak says "no" it was NO! We had a Litvak teacher once and it would have been easier to move Mount Everest than to get her to change her mind. Here, let me give you ah f'rinstance. One Friday, she was getting ready to give us a test and all of a sudden there was a fire drill. Talk about being *ungeshpart* (stubborn) - she made us take the papers with us just in case it was a real fire and said we would have had time to take the test outside waiting for the fire engines to arrive. She was going to give that test even if the whole school burned down!

But why talk - it's a new world! If the Litvaks and the Galitzianas have now learned to live with one another in peace - you know - there's *takeh* hope for the world!

PROGRESS: WHO NEEDS IT?

Years ago, you could squeeze a few tomatoes to see if they were ripe - but today, they spend millions on television to tell us what is good for us.

E PRIDE OURSELVES IN TODAY'S WORLD ON the fantastic progress we have made. So, let me ask you – what kind of progress?

In the supermarket today, everything is covered with plastic or cellophane. In the years not too long past – there was the human contact. If you wanted to buy a honeydew – you went in - squeezed a couple of melons and shoen - you knew! You knocked on one or two and if you didn't get an answer you knew right away - it was ripe! That was shopping!

In the old days when you went into a store you were

greeted with a smile by a clerk. You felt wanted. Today, you walk in and a *farbissener* (mean person) clerk stands at the check-out counter and gives you a look like you just woke him or her up.

Even in the banks, years ago you could walk in and fill a fountain pen. And the guard would smile and even help you. Today - forget it! No more ink, just ball point pens - that they chain down! Right away they start off with the assumption that you're a criminal! You're guilty before you're proven innocent!

In the years past, you walked into a store and a clerk waited on you in minutes. Today, you go into a supermarket to buy bananas, they turn ripe while waiting at the check-out counter!

In the days not so long past when you bought a Dixie cup of ice cream - not only did you get ice cream but you also got a picture of a movie star. Who had to buy bubble gum to save cards? We played with those Dixie cup cards like they were money! Today, you go in to buy ice cream and walk out with a box of air called "ice milk."

In yesteryears if Mama needed something in the grocery store, we'd run in - knew just where to find it on the shelf - grab the item and yell out, "My mother said to put it in the book..."

The grocer would mark it down and at the end of the week Mama would straighten out with the grocer.

Today - forget it - who keeps a book? Of course maybe a handful of the smaller "Mama-Papa" stores may do this - but that personal touch, for the most part, is gone.

Today's supermarkets have that sterile effect like you're in a hospital.

In our years when you walked into a store - the aroma of the various foods were the invitation to buy. When you walked into an appetizing store - you were greeted with the smell of pickles! Today - the stores put pickles in a jar. *Nu*, I ask you, how can you adjust to such a thing? And then when you try to get one pickle out, *gevald!*

In our day when Mama bought a breakfast cereal she bought it because it had nutrients in it. Today's mothers buy cereals for their small fry because of the premiums. The kids come to shop with their mothers but don't ask for trade names – they ask for "the cereal with the submarine or the ones with the rockets." Who looks for nourishment anymore? The kids get today's nourishment from bubble gum!

Let me tell you a funny story. I have a friend whose little one doesn't eat a thing at home. But when she takes him shopping the little monster eats his way through the supermarket! Honest! First she stops off at the fruit counter and the little one starts munching on a fruit. Then they work their way past the cheese counters and he finds a cheese that interests him – and then to the appetizing counter for a nosh of pickles. Last month the kid put on four pounds, and the store failed!

Today, they actually design the stores for the little ones. Even the shopping carts have seats for them. Listen who wouldn't get an appetite being pushed around a supermarket?

The smells of yesterday are gone! Today's stores are spotlessly clean – when you come in expecting a fresh bread smell or pickle smell – you smell disinfectant!

But listen – it's clean! We survived in another world, a world of smells.

The only real smells left today are in delicatessens. When you pass the hot dog grill section – *oy is dot geshmack!*

Let me ask you, what smell could be more exciting than hot dogs on a grill with knishes at their side next to the pastrami? Listen, where would a delicatessen be without a smell? The non-Jewish delicatessens don't smell, but a kosher deli – *gevald!*

A short time ago somebody invented a machine that cooked hot dogs so quickly that they didn't have a chance to smell. That's like making a bagel without the hole in the middle! They called that progress. That's like going to the moon and forgetting to bring back moon rocks!

In those years past, you'd walk into an A & P store and smell freshly roasted coffee. Oy, was that a smell. Today – everything is in a vacuum-packed container.

Even soda – today it all comes in cans or plastic bottles that you have to bring back. A bottle of soda with a knish – dot was something!

I had a friend who was a chemist and years ago he came up with an idea of putting smells – delicious cooking smells – in an aerosol can. When women prepared TV dinners (kosher of course) they could spray the house with a cugel smell – or maybe a *hockfleish* smell – or even a challah smell. So when their husbands came home, they felt their wives were *balabustehs!*

He put up the smells in some cans and tried to sell them. So you know what happened, some nut came along and put out a product that killed the smells in a house. Did you ever hear of Air-Wick? *Nu* – go be smart.

Smells are still very important. Let me ask you, did you ever buy a new car? So tell me – what's the first thing that strikes you when you step into a new car – the upholstery? The fancy dashboard? *Ah nechtiger tug* (forget it) – it's the new car smell! And that, takeh, comes in a can. Honest! Ask any new car dealer – they give every car a "new smell" spritz – and shoen! My cousin bought a can of the "new car smell" and sold his old car in less than 24 hours!

When Air-Wick first came out – my dopey little brother Berel decided to see how good it really was. So he cut open a clove a of garlic and put it next to the bottle of Air-Wick. He wanted to see who would win.

Who do you think won? The garlic, of course. In less than 24 hours – the Air-Wick smelled from the garlic. And let me ask you, did you ever smell Air-Wick saturated with garlic smell? *Oy vey - kenst brechen!* (You can get real sick).

Today's world is a sterile world. You can buy aerosol cans that bring the outdoors into your home. *Nu*, so let me ask you, have you smelled the outdoors lately? If they could put delicatessen smells into a can and spritz it around the house, that would be a smell!

But why talk – it's a new world – with new smells.

THE PRETZEL LADY'S CHANUKAH

I guess there was one near every school in those years...you know the pretzel sellers, with their huge wicker baskets. Remember?

THOSE WONDERFUL LITTLE PEOPLE WHO SOLD those huge salty pretzels near every school were very much a part of New York's long past.

I remember the lady who sold pretzels near our school in the Bronx. Regardless of the weather this sweet little old woman stood on the corner with her basket of pretzels trying to earn her way. Our pretzel seller looked like someone's grandmother. She had the most beautiful silver-gray hair I have every seen, and her small round face almost like a cherub, was always a bright red in the freezing winter months.

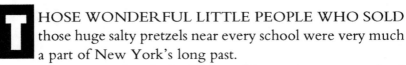

I'll never forget the year we were finishing up school on the last day before the winter vacation. It also happened to be the first night of Chanukah. As we waited for the school day to end we could see snowflakes start to fall. Who heard the teacher? Our eyes were glued on the steam-covered windows that caught the gentle snow. Each little flake landed ever so gently on the panes of glass.

Finally, the 3 o'clock bell rang. Oh, what joy – the start of the holiday. As we raced down the iron steps of the school into the snow-filled street, the air was alive with screams of joy from the children greeting the snow. Some threw their books to the ground to make their first real snowball of the season. What an adventure!

The air was brisk and the flakes fell, tickling our nose and ears. As we walked toward the corner, there she was. We always saved two cents for a stop at the pretzel lady. It was almost like a ritual.

The pretzels were covered with a white sheet of paper to protect them from the weather. The old lady had a scarf covering her head with a knot tied neatly beneath her chin. She wore a heavy sweater with a shawl covering her shoulders.

On this day we made our usual stop. She smiled warmly as we approached. She lifted the white piece of paper that sheltered her pretzels from the falling snow and said, "I saved the warm ones for you. I have them wrapped in paper. I know you like the pretzels warm."

We felt so proud – getting this VIP treatment. She leaned into her basket and withdrawing the pretzels said softly, almost to herself, "Yes, yes, I always save the warm ones for my children."

What a wonderful feeling. Actually most of the kids who went to our school bought pretzels from her. They were all "her children."

We made our purchase and as we turned to walk away she said softly, "Have a wonderful happy Chanukah, children. Dress warm and stay healthy. Don't get sick from the snow."

Yup, we were her children. We never really knew if she was Jewish or not, but since she wished us a good holiday I concluded she was. Most of the other pretzel sellers on the other corners were usually old Italian gentlemen who would also sell hot chestnuts and sweet potatoes in the winter. Our pretzel lady only sold pretzels.

As we walked away, my little brother Berel commented sadly in between chomps on his pretzel, "She must be a pretty poor lady."

"I guess so," I added, chewing away as we walked toward our house.

"Think she's Jewish?" Berel asked.

"I guess so - she wished us a Happy Chanukah," I replied.

We walked as the snow continued to come down with full fury. Berel was concerned. "Do you think she made enough money today selling pretzels to buy candles for a Chanukah menorah?" he questioned. "She had a lot of pretzels left."

"Gee, I dunno..." I sighed, getting a little more concerned. "Mama's got an extra box," he volunteered. "One or two are broken but that don't make any difference. I'll run home and get the candles, you go back and tell her to wait for me," he said as he began to run to our house."

I ran back to the corner where she sold the pretzels but she was gone. I looked around and saw her trudging through the snow about a block away lugging her heavy basket of unsold pretzels. I figured I would follow her, find out where she lived and then go back for Berel, otherwise we'd lose her trail. She continued walking about three more blocks and then turned into an alley between two old apartment houses. By the time I reached the alley she was gone, but there were fresh tracks in the snow that led to one small door in the basement section of one of the buildings.

I looked in a window and sure enough there she was. There was a bare wooden table on one side of the small room and two orange crates she used for chairs in another corner. Near the broken-down sink were two little gas burners. There was a coffee pot on one burner. On her table was a small inexpensive Chanukah menorah.

I started to walk back to the street to find Berel. By the time I reached the school, Berel was standing on the corner. "Where'd ya go?" he shouted. "I thought you ran out on me," he blubbered.

I explained what had happened and reassured him that I knew where she lived. We began to run back to the alley between the two apartment houses. When we got to the door we knocked, but there was no answer. We knocked a little harder, but still no answer.

Berel ran to the window then shouted, "She's lying on the floor!" I ran to the window and could see her stretched out near the sink.

We tried to open the door but it was locked and we couldn't budge it. We both ran out into the street to get help. Just then a man was passing by. We told him what we saw and he followed us into the alley and looked through the window. He tried the door, then with all his might he broke the door down. We ran into the apartment. Everything smelled from gas. He shouted, "Quick, open the window." He ran to the stove and shut off the gas jet. The pot of coffee she was boiling had run over and put out the flame, but the gas continued to flow.

The man dragged the old lady toward the door for fresh air. He began slapping her face and suddenly she started to moan. She was coming to. We were in time. In a few minutes she was able to sit up and asked what had happened. The man told her that we saw her on the floor and called him for help. She started to smile and offered us a free pretzel. She had recognized us.

The gas fumes were cleared out and we closed the window. Berel took out the package of Chanukah candles and told her we had an extra box and thought that she might need some.

She smiled warmly and said that she had forgotten to make her purchase of candles and that she wanted to pay us for the candles, in pretzels. Berel had put away three pretzels thus far, so we politely refused.

She put two candles in the Chanukah holder that was set on the table. She then moved them to a dark corner of the room. She said a prayer and lit the candles.

A warm glow filled the room. The man stood by beaming. As the glow of the candles became brighter the man noticed a very old book on the shelf. He picked it up and looked at it curiously.

Most of the pages were frayed and the binding was gone. It looked like junk.

As he began looking through the book she said, "That's a very old book. Old like me. Worthless!"

The man continued to look at the book then said, "Would you sell me this book? I'm a book dealer and sell old books and religious articles. I would be more than happy to give you two hundred dollars for this book!"

The woman looked at him with disbelief. "It is an old book. Do you think it has any value?"

"Will you sell it to me?" the man asked again.

"Let me give it to you, after all, you saved my life." she said.

"Oh, no that would not be fair, you would be taking away my *mitzvah*," he retorted as he put his hand in his pocket and pulled out a handful of bills. He counted out two hundred dollars, handed it to her, then gave my brother and myself five dollars each. "This is my Chanukah gift to you boys for being so alert and thoughtful."

We walked from the house together as the snow continued to fall. We felt rich! As we walked down the street the man ran ahead of us and said he was late. We watched as he moved though the snow swiftly. When he came toward the corner, he passed a garbage can, paused for a second, then threw the old book into the can, and continued on his way.

It was then we realized that he did not want the book, but wanted to do something for that little old woman, without embarrassing her.

We never did see that man again even though we were certain he lived in the neighborhood. We never knew who he was, but he certainly made the old lady happy.

When the vacation was over and we returned to school, we looked for our pretzel lady once more, but she wasn't there.

That first afternoon we came back to school we walked over to the place where she lived. No one was in the apartment. Just then, the superintendent of one of the buildings happened by and asked us what we were doing in the alley. We told him we were looking for the pretzel lady.

He looked at us and said sadly, "Oh, she passed away a few days ago. She was a wonderful lady and loved children very much."

He turned away and didn't say another word.

We walked home sadly. I don't think I shall ever forget that wonderful pretzel lady, nor the stranger who made her last days on this earth happy ones.

OFF TO THE MOUNTAINS

Today, if somebody wants to go to the mountains, you hop in the wagon and in less than two hours you're in the mountains! But in yesterday's world, to go to the mountains - like Mama said, "Dot wuz an expedition!"

IN THOSE YEARS, THE FOLKS SCRIMPED AND saved all winter long so that we might spend a couple weeks in the mountains - to drink in *der fresher luft*, the fresh air.

I'll never forget one summer when we were to go to the mountains for two weeks to a small *koch alain* (where one cooked alone) hotel. First, let me explain. A *koch alain* hotel really wasn't a hotel - it was a big boarding house. They called it 'ah hotel' strictly for status. The *koch alain* was a world unto itself. It had one big community kitchen. Here, each family had a stove with a small cooking area. One burner never worked –it was always clogged with grease from, like the owner would say, "from der *chazzer* (the pig) dot was here last year." Next to each stove was a small kitchen table covered with a tiny piece of oil cloth, usually red, white and yellow plaid, that had seen better days. In some cases more than one family would share a stove. Let me tell you something – it was like cooking in Madison Square Garden. Everybody knew everybody else's *tzuris* (problems). The stoves were lined up against a wall like so many soldiers and everybody cooked. Gevald! What smells! On Fridays when the women made gefilte fish that community kitchen was symphony of smells.

Papa worked overtime all winter long so we should be able to afford these two weeks of "luxury" and drink in the country air. As we began the ritual of preparation for our vacation, Papa would go down to the cellar in our building and shlep upstairs the old trunk that an uncle had given us years ago. The trunk would be filled with everything that we might possibly need for our two week stay. Then a big European suitcase that accompanied Papa from Europe years before, was packed to overflowing. The whole tribe would sit on the suitcase so that Papa would be able to tie it up with rope he brought from his place!

The next step was to make arrangements with a car-service man. Let me tell you, the car-service men in those years were a breed unto themselves. The car-service man was usually a retired taxi driver who managed to get hold of the largest and oldest decrepit cars to 'run to the mountains.' Usually they bought up old funeral cars for a bargain! Those old time cars would have exterior trunk racks in the back that were usually overloaded with suitcases which were covered with a piece of canvas and tied with a heavy rope. In the back seat of the car they would squeeze in three or four adults. Then there would be the two little fold–up seats for two more passengers, but if you stuck a board in between the two seats you could squeeze in another person. In the front, the driver sat with two adults or for good measure a little kid squeezed in between the driver and those seated next to him.

Let me tell you - comfortable it wasn't - rustic yes - but *gevald*, a pleasure trip it never was! The old cars they used were always either Cadillacs or Packards, but they all had one thing in common - when they went up the Wurtsboro Hills - they would all boil over. In fact, when those cars just saw the Wurtsboro Hills from a distance, they would drop dead just thinking about the climb. *Takeh*, it was *ah rachmones* (pity) on the car!

In the summer around the Wurtsboro Hills there were cars all along the side of the road - panting away with the radiators sending up billows of steam. Sometimes, the drivers would pull over - let the car cool down for a few minutes then ask the passengers to get out and walk up the hill in back of the car. It looked like a funeral. Listen - if you were as old as some of the cars, you would puff and pant also. More often than not, the drivers would ask the men in the car to help push the car up the mountain.

Those old time drivers really had a system. When a car had an unusually heavy load they would pull over, let the passengers out and drive the car up the mountain just with the suitcases and trunks. When the driver got to the top of the hill he would take off the suitcases and trunks, put them at the side of the road, and then go down the hill to pick up the passengers. When they got to the top of the hill, they would reload the car, then go on until they hit the next impossible hill. Like I said before - it was an experience!

The only thing you could depend on with the independent car-service was their undependability. If the dispatcher said be ready at eight - you could be certain the car would show up at noon. If they agreed to take you up for a certain price - by the time they got to the house - there was always something extra to charge you for! *Nu* - so Papa and Mama made the arrangements with "Sam's Cars To The Mountains" store on Southern Boulevard in the Bronx. The store was a former appetizing store and - gevald did that place smell.

"Listen – I'm all filled up for the day you want," Sam exclaimed as Mama and Papa made the arrangements, "but if you want to pay a few dollars extra I might be able to make an extra trip."

Normally they charged nine dollars a person and half price for children, but for the special trip it was two dollars extra per person and fifty cents extra for children.

"Okay – but listen, be ready at five in the morning – you'll be the first stop," Sam exclaimed as we left the store.

"Don't worry, we'll be ready," we all chimed out. We were so excited!

I'll never forget that morning. We were up about three A.M. Mama made us breakfast and then washed the dishes. Then she began mopping the floor that had been mopped the day before. "Listen – if burglars break in while we're away – it shouldn't look dirty when the policemen come," Mama rationalized. My little brother Berel went to the window to wait and watch for the car-service man.

Nu – so four o'clock came and four-thirty and then five and then six and then seven and still no Sam the car-service man. Finally about noon – a monstrous relic of a car piled high with suitcases and trunks rounded the corner, panting and breathing hard.

Papa told Sam, "Listen, you said five, how come you're so late? I thought we were supposed to be the first pick-up!"

Sam was angry. "Listen – for what you're paying you want I should be early? You should have my headaches! I had to make a pick up in Brooklyn so what should I do – take you first and shlep you and the children all over Brooklyn? Listen, come, it's late."

Papa shrugged his shoulders, "Nu, so give me a hand down with the trunk and the suitcase."

Sam looked angry. "What are you talking? What trunk and suitcase? Can't you see I'm loaded? Where should I put it – on my head? What are you talking?"

Papa was getting angry now. "Sam, listen, I told you we were going to the mountains for two weeks – should we wear the same clothes for two weeks?"

"Listen, it will cost you extra for the trunk and the suitcase. I'm loaded up already!" Sam snapped.

Papa was angry now. "What extra? You made a price with us – you asked extra and I gave you. You came six hours late and now you want to charge me extra for the suitcase and the trunk?"

But this time the passengers in the car were getting edgy. "Sam," one called out, "listen if the man doesn't want to pay – let him stay. Who needs him? Come – it's getting late!"

Papa turned to Sam and asked with finality, "Will you take the suitcase and trunk for what we agreed upon?"

Sam snapped, "Absolutely not! It will cost extra! Dot's my final word!"

My little brother Berel began to cry – he thought Sam was the only one who went to the mountains. But Papa was angry. "Please go – you're not the only hacky!" Papa shouted with blood rushing to his face.

Sam turned and muttered – "*Herst ah meiseh* – a man orders the car and then decides not to go. Did you ever hear of such a thing?"

The passengers jammed into the back of the car must have been his relatives. They called out, "Cheapskate – you should pay the extra – we did!"

Sam pulled away from the curb with his squealing load leaving a trail of black smoke behind.

We walked with Papa toward 179th Street and saw another store marked, "Greenberg – Always Cars To The Mountains."

We walked in and there was Greenberg in this huge empty store sitting behind an ancient broken down desk. This store was formerly a dry-goods store, so there were no smells.

"Yes? Can I help you?" Mr. Greenberg asked.

"I want to go to the mountains," Papa said.

"Dot's der business!" Greenberg smiled, as he opened

a huge book with blank pages, "When would you like to go?"

Papa smiled, "Right now!"

"Right now?" Greenberg raised his eyebrows. "How come instantaneously?" Papa explained the problem we had with Sam and repeated the question, "Can you take the family up today – in fact as soon as possible?"

"Listen, instant service like this I don't have. My car left already. Maybe tomorrow I could pick you up at five o'clock…"

"Never mind," Papa sighed – it's just that the children were so disappointed."

Just then a cute little puppy ran out from a corner of the desk and started playing with my little brother Berel. As Papa started walking toward the door dejectedly, Greenberg called out, "Mister – let me make you ah proposition. I don't work like Sam the Mountain Man – I'm a one price business. I would make a trip now to the mountains if you wouldn't object to doing me a favor. You see I got ah customer who wants me to bring her dog up to the mountains but nobody wants to sit in the car with a dog. But, if the children could play with it and you wouldn't mind – I'll take you as soon as I finish my coffee!"

Papa smiled, "Vee fil – how much?"

Greenberg smiled back, "Nine dollars an adult and half for the children."

"How much extra for the trunk or suitcase?" Papa questioned.

"What trunk and suitcases – who charges for suitcases and trunks?" Greenberg questioned. "Dot comes with the trip."

He took a little leash from a nail that hung on the wall and put it on the little dog's collar. "Come get in –I'll take my best car. Where is your wife?"

We got into an almost brand new Cadillac and he drove us to the house to pick up Mama and the baggage. The trunk and suitcase were loaded on the back and we were headed for the mountains. *Shoen*, instant service.

The dog was called Chaver Shainer and as we road along, Greenberg kept asking, "*Nu*, so how's Chaver Shainer?"

He was a jolly old timer and it was really a pleasant trip. The dog fell asleep as soon as it got in the car. When we reached the Wurtsboro Hills, the new car went up the hill like a bullet. As we reached the half-way mark - sure enough among the cars steaming over that were pulled over to the side was Sam's car.

We slowed down as we passed Sam. His car had a broken axle plus the boiling over radiator. Greenberg smiled - and turned to Papa - *Zest* - dot's Sam - he give the whole business a bad name."

As we passed we all waved good-bye to the passengers who were sitting on their suitcases at the side of the road waiting for a mechanic to come and tow Sam in.

We finally reached the mountains and sure enough Greenberg's wife was staying at the same *koch alain* hotel we were to say at. Mama and Papa became fast friends with the Greenbergs - a friendship that lasted for years.

As soon as we pulled up, the dog jumped out and took off for *yenem velt* - another world. We never did find little Chaver Shainer!

PIANOS AND VIOLINS

I think every Jewish family in our neighborhood had a piano.
If they didn't have a piano they probably had a violin.

IRST OF ALL, WHY DO I SAY EVERY JEWISH family had a piano - were we such a rich generation? Of course not. For the most part we were poor. Our parents barely made a living. But, when it came to giving the children culture - money was no object. When they moved into a house, the parents would scrimp and save to purchase a piano for their children. After all, what parents wanted to deprive a child of culture? Then as the children grew up and got married the piano began gathering dust in the corner and the families began to move to smaller apartments. After all those years and with those ancient buildings continuously settling on their foundations - it was impossible to get the piano through the door. The door was on an angle. To hire the piano movers to take the piano out through the window - who needed it - the children were already grown! Who would be left to play? So the pianos stayed when the new families moved in. And when another Jewish family moved in - after all, who would complain that there was a piano already in the apartment? It was advertised as "partially furnished." And so the next generation of little ones began their musical culture simply because a building was settling.

The families who had violins had a different story. Many of the old timers brought along a violin if they played in the old country. In Europe, a violin was part of the culture - but in America - who needed it, unless you were a real musician. *Nu* - so who needed a violin laying in the closet gathering dust? The violins were usually given to the first family with a little boy who moved on the floor.

After a period of time, when the little one put the violin aside the family usually passed it on to a cousin - so it should remain in the family.

In those years you could tell a Jewish neighborhood. All you had to do was walk down the street around three-thirty in the afternoon and hear the kids banging away on a piano with "March Militaire" or "Hanon's Exercises." Occasionally, you'd hear the "Minute Waltz" being slaughtered.

My sisters played that Minute Waltz in such a way that Frederic Chopin, must still be spinning in his grave. *Gevald* what they did with that waltz!

Every time we got company, Mama would have my sisters put on a recital consisting of the "Edelweis Glide," "March Militaire" and the "Minute Waltz." Occasionally they played a Jewish song, but Mama made them stop. The way they played it, she didn't want the neighbors to think we were anti-Semitic!

From time to time Mama would call in the piano tuner - she didn't believe the sounds coming out of our piano were all my sister's fault. But it didn't help -*takeh* they were that terrible!

We had a kid next door - Davey Mermelstein - who played the violin. That kid hocked away on his violin with a vengeance. His father was a shochet - so people thought he was slaughtering chickens in their apartment! I want you to know that Davey got sounds out of the violin that make the sound of squeaking chalk on a blackboard sound melodious!

I'll never forget the time his music teacher gave him a selection that had a piano part to it. I think the piece was called "Il Baccio." When his teacher played along with him, it was a nice song. When Davey played - we thought the Italians down the block were gonna attack! *Gevald*, he was so terrible!

As horrible as he was on the violin, that's how great a sling shot man he was. Davey was able to get little pieces of cardboard and shoot them out from between the strings with deadly aim. When he played around for our benefit, because we used to come up to watch him practice - he was incredible. He told his mother he was practicing "pizzicato." But, what he did with that violin and little pieces of cardboard, was amazing!

Anyway, his teacher gave him that "Il Baccio" piece and his mother came to Mama and suggested that one of my sisters learn the piano part. Together they would entertain visitors on the weekends. This would have been a great idea - if the folks were interested in breaking a lease - but for entertainment - *gevald*! We always wondered who had that many relatives they wanted to get even with.

So my sister began learning the piano part. Now, if you know anything about the piano accompaniment for a violin, you would know that the piano part simply goes "oom-pa-pa, oom-pa-pa." The melody is carried by the violin. I want you to know when my sister played her own pieces that had melody, she murdered the music. So you can imagine what was coming out of the old piano! The super thought the neighbors were calling for more steam! In those years when people wanted more steam they knocked on the pipes. And come to think of it the knocking on the pipes had more melody than the noise that was coming out of the piano.

After two weeks, Mrs. Mermelstein said Davey was ready to perform his part and asked Mama if my sister knew hers.

"Of course she knows her part," Mama explained proudly. Of course she knew her part? Baloney! She wouldn't have known that part if she were pumping a player piano! Listen, a musician she wasn't.

Nu, so David and my eldest sister counted off. "One-two - three..."

That first note was great. It sounded as if someone had caught a cat's tail in a door! The second note was even worse!

"Wait-wait," my sister halted the music. "We're not in time with each other," as if that mattered.

So she counted off once more and the music began. It was some piece of music! I don't know if it was simply coincidental - but half way through the piece the light bulb in our chandelier exploded! Honest! Davey thought some-one was shooting at him from the window. He hid behind my sister!

They interrupted the "murder" for a few minutes when my sister who was a year older than Davey, counseled, "I don't think we are in tune - try tuning the violin." This she said with such authority, you'd swear she knew what she was talking about.

Listen - why not - everything else failed. So Davey twisted a few pegs of his violin while my sister was playing notes that were supposed to match his strings. Now they were ready once more. *Shoen* - the violin was tuned.

"One-two-three," my sister counted once more and the onslaught began again in earnest.

By the tenth time - either we were going deaf or maybe they were getting better - but, it didn't sound bad. The two kids put in some very original touches - like Davey shooting a piece of cardboard from his A string during a four measure rest sequence. Mama couldn't get over how beautiful the music was. Mrs. Mermelstein sighed, "*Oy*, if my mother-in-law, may she rest in peace, was only alive to hear her little *einikel*." (grandson).

We could never figure that one out - we didn't think anybody could bear such a grudge. Gosh, were those kids terrible - but heaven forbid we should say a word! One day my little brother Berel giggled while the kids were playing, and Mama gave him such a shot in the mouth - I think the swelling still hasn't gone down.

A few weeks later, when Davey's teacher came, Mrs. Mermelstein told him how great the two played. So she gave Davey a new piece with piano accompaniment - this one was the "Elegy," I think by Massenet. You heard it?

After the first week of Davey's *kvetching* (squeezing) out the melody, he came down with the accompaniment and my sister sight-read the entire piece! Of course, when they played it a second time there was entirely different accompaniment. And the third time it was still different. One thing you had to say for those kids - their music was not repetitious. Always original!

By the fifth time they played the piece my sister discovered she was still reading the accompaniment sheet from "Il Baccio" - but it didn't make any difference. When you played "Il Baccio" slowly, it sounded great! Today, that's the big thing - playing two different melodies at the same time. See how far ahead of the times those kids were.

Davey continued to play violin and as the years passed either we started to mellow or the kid became good. During the summer months he got a job playing in the mountains with a band. He didn't make much - in fact, the band he was playing with had to pay the hotel owner a modest fee for food. They just wanted to play for the experience. But it didn't make much difference because most of the guests at this hotel were over eighty and those were the years before hearing aids.

As the years passed, Davey went to college, became an

accountant and simply played the violin for his own enjoyment. My sister soon shied away from the piano for, what she said, were more important things to occupy her mind with. The old piano just settled down to dormancy for years until Mama decided to give my little brother Berel lessons. That didn't last too long, because Berel figured out a way to shoot little pieces of cardboard from the strings of the piano. And this wasn't easy! Of course, he was never as good as Davey was with the violin, but Mama and Papa agreed the piano deserved a better fate than that.

As the years passed and my sisters and Berel married, Mama and Papa still had the piano. When it came time to move, there was no room in their new smaller apartment. It meant that the old piano with those wonderful memories, would have to be left behind. My sisters lived in Pittsburgh, Berel *in yenem velt* (way out) on Long Island and I, who lived fairly close to civilization on Long Island, won the piano.

And now, in all its glory, it stands in a corner of my house. All of my children and their friends banged on it. Whenever we thought we heard a combination of notes that sounded like a song, we seriously thought we were growing a genius. But that was the extent of it. No geniuses.

When my sisters come to visit - they play the accompaniment to "Il Baccio" or some "Elegy" - nothing fancy mind you - but just enough to let that old piano know that we haven't forgotten.

A few years ago, my grandson figured out how to get the dog to walk on the piano keyboard. And you know something -I think that little mutt had more music in her soul than my whole family. When he put a few dog yummies on the keyboard - the dog was able to tap out the first four notes to "Il Baccio." Without music!

Nu - but why go on - my sisters got their culture - as did my little tribe. I've often wondered - if that piano could only talk - what it would say? Probably, "*Gevald!*"

ULTRA MODERN HEADACHES

When the astronauts landed on the moon they said, "One small step for a man, a giant leap for mankind." But they weren't thinking about how the modern inventions put our generation into obscurity.

WHEN WE WERE KIDS, AND IF WE HAD TO OPEN a door, we pulled on the door knob and shoen, the door opened! Today, when you go to a supermarket, who knows from doorknobs? Try and find one! Today, you step on a rubber mat and like magic the door is supposed to open. It opens for everybody except when I need to get it open! Then it does one of two things - it either hits me in the face as I go halfway through the exit - or it stays closed so tight the manager can't even open it!

For generations, people who owned private houses had

two doors on their garage that you opened simply by pulling on them. Then, all of a sudden, somebody invented doors that rise automatically by a radio signal device you keep in your car. Very nice - *ut* is progress! My friend who just bought a new television set found out that when he turns it on he opens his neighbor's garage door. Every time he changes channels, garage doors for a block in all directions go up and down! Honest! It's a scream! When you go to his house nobody watches television –we just sit on his porch and watch the garage doors on his block, open and close!

Let me ask you, years ago when a woman wanted to make a potato kugel or latkes, what would she do? She would take *a ribeisen* (a grater) to grate the potatoes and onions. Today, with all the modern inventions, everybody uses a blender. *Ut* is a modern way! *Ah nechtiger tug!* (like heck!) Did you ever taste a kugel or potato *latkes* made on a blender - real poison! *Latkes* made on a *ribeisen* are *latkes*! The lumps give it character! A blender pulverizes the potatoes. Listen - why talk - it's not the same!

Years ago when Mama wanted to wash clothes she took out the *vash breitel* (washing board), stuck it in the sink, and with a bar of brown soap began to rub. The clothes came out spotlessly clean. Who knew from "ring around the collar?" Who needed detergents and the other perfumes they put in the soaps today? Let me ask you - why don't they invent an automatic *vash breitel*?

Years ago, a modern home was considered modern if it had an ice box - most people like us simply had a fruit box on the window sill where Mama kept the perishible foods. Today, the average American home has a refrigerator and a great many modern homes have a freezer. *Ut* is also progress! Then, the second we get a little snow or an ice storm the electricity is cut off and a small fortune in food has to be thrown out! You know, if we stayed with the ice box and the *shissel* or even the window box we would probably be ahead!

Throughout our history our people never believed in

major changes. Listen, throughout the ages that wasn't our style and we aren't ready to change. Today when a company opens another fancy chain store they put a small fortune into the fanciest fixtures. Then they turn around and sell the same old stale merchandise for a fortune. But, when one of our people goes into business, it's simply for selling merchandise at prices people can afford.

Here, let me give you an example - and this isn't a commercial. A few years ago a group of Chassidic boys went into business and opened up a photo supply place. They didn't even rent a store - they rented a loft - one flight up. They put up four walls and stocked the place with hundreds of cameras and all kinds of photo equipment. They have been doing land office business ever since they opened. Just four walls! The money they didn't spend on fixtures they turned back to their customers in reduced prices and you can't purchase a piece of camera equipment for less in this city! They close early Friday afternoon, stay closed on Shabbos and open Sunday when you can't find a soul in midtown. Yet you have to stand in line to get in - rain, sleet or snow! *Zest* - without inventions - just four walls!

Here, talk about *chatchkehs* (gadgets). A friend recently bought a fancy car with all the gadgets in the world. Nu, so last summer, in the middle of the August heat wave with temperatures in the high 90's he couldn't get his air conditioner to go on. It was the latest and most modern they made. *Nu*, so he fiddled around under the dashboard and all of a sudden the heating system went on with a blast. *Gevald* did that thing go on! No matter what he did, he couldn't turn it off. It was late, so he drove all the way back to Jersey with the heating system blasting him in the face in the 90 degree temperature. Then, adding insult to injury, last week in the heart of the snowstorm, when he went to turn on the heater, he hit another button and the air conditioner went on! And no matter what he did he couldn't shut it off. When he got home he was frozen solid!

My son bought a new chain and lock for his bike. The

man in the bike store said it was the "latest invention" in theft - proof devices. The instructions on the box said, "Only you can open this lock!" Nu, so like a good citizen, when I had to go to the bakery and wanted to save fuel, I took the bike. When I got to the bakery, I locked up the bike with the new modern chain. I must have spent an hour trying to get that lock open. Forget it! I wound up shlepping the bike 10 blocks back to my house. Then when I left the bike outside of my house to bring in the bread and rolls - you guessed it -someone stole the lock and chain! The bike they left!

Now you know, I'm not one to talk - but today's modern radios with their new inventions are a menace. My middle son recently bought a fancy modern radio with a clock that puts you to sleep with music and wakes you up to music. So one night when I came home late and passed by his room the radio was still on, and he was fast asleep. Listen, am I a partner with Con Edison? So I tiptoed into the room to shut the set off. *Gevald*! I want you to know, I must have turned every dial, button, switch and transistor in that darn set but it wouldn't go off! Finally I had to pull out the plug. A simple on-off switch they couldn't afford to put into the darn thing! And of course the kid overslept that morning because he depended on the radio to wake him.

Once upon a time when Mama went shopping she took along a little leatherette shopping bag Papa had made for her to carry home the groceries. Today, because we want them to use fewer trees to make paper, a great many stores have stopped "double- bagging." Now you go three feet and the whole bottom drops out! On all the cash registers they have signs that say, "New improved shopping bags - no double-bagging necessary." Listen - let them go back to the old unimproved shopping bags or paper bags we used before double bagging!

Everything today is so modern - once upon a time when you made a phone call an operator with a cheery voice got on the phone and gave you your number. Today it's all different. Do you know if you want to get the number of "information" you can't get it! Honest. The other day I forgot the number for information, so I dialed the operator. I asked her if she could give me the number to get information. She said, "Please dial information - we are not permitted to give out telephone numbers." I figured the information number was unlisted! Who knows in today's world?

Let me ask you something - did you see those "new improved" push-button telephones? Let me ask you, what was wrong with dial telephones where the index finger got a little exercise every once in a while?

My neighbor got one of those phones and one day his cat accidentally knocked the new phone off its cradle. The cat then accidentally walked on the little delicate buttons - and my neighbor was billed for two calls to California! Go tell the telephone company his cat made the calls!

Listen - it's a new world - filled with improvements we could have lived without. Here - do I have to go far - in the plant where The Jewish Press is printed we have the most ultra - modern equipment, machinery and computers to set the type. When we printed the old way, with linotype machines, we had some typographical errors. Listen, it happens. Normally a newspaper is entitled to 10% of all their stories having typographical errors. Since we have the ultra-modern new inventions producing the paper - we have 20% typographical errors.

In the mail room when we had a great many people putting addresses on the papers that were to be sent out, sometimes they would make a small mistake and ship out an extra paper to one person. Listen, it happens - no one is perfect. Today with a computer setting the names - if the computer gives 'ah hiccup' - one subscriber could get as many as 60 papers mailed to his house. Oy would his postman have a time getting them into the mailbox!

But why talk - it's a new world with new inventions - if we can only survive them.

SCHOOL'S OUT

Millions of parents ask themselves in early June, weeks before the summer vacation begins – when does school start again?

Y THE TIME JULY ARRIVES, THE SOUND OF "NO more pencils, no more books, no more teacher's rotten looks," has already faded away. School is over for the next ten weeks! And, if the weather gives a little tinkle – and an 'X' or 'R' rated movie is the only thing playing in the neighborhood – *gevald*! The kids climb the walls!

As far as the little ones are concerned – they have four thousand toys to play with, toys that cost a mint. *Nu*, so when the first rainy day hits they look you square in the eye and whine – "I got nuttin' to do!"

Today how many families sacrifice all year long to save up enough to go to the beach as our folks did years ago? So the first thing that happens after all the heartache of saving for this little vacation for the *kinder*, the kids begin to nag – "I got no one to play with – they only got girls (or boys) here!"

I'll never forget the times Mama and Papa scrimped and saved all year just so we could go to Rockaway – to 'take ah room.' If we didn't have much money that particular year we took 'ah roomkeleh' (that meant a smaller room with my little brother Berel having to sleep in the bathtub!)

Mama would console him with, "*Az mir vet leben*, (if we live) next year you'll have 'ah porch room'."

A porch room, for the uninformed was the cheapest room in the boarding house because its windows opened on to the porch. And whenever anybody sat on the porch all night long and talked, you simply couldn't fall asleep. But for little brother Berel this was a godsend! That little monster had ears like a radar set – and a head like a sponge. He knew everybody's business.

For him the porch room was better than television – after all, television wasn't even invented in those years! He would lie in bed listening to everything. And don't think he didn't have a variety of things to choose from.

When Sarah Goodstein was becoming engaged to Irving Fogelman, Berel monitored the dialogue. In the morning, for breakfast, we couldn't wait for the little dummy to open his mouth and fill us all in on the new events of the night before!

Mama would give *ah geshrie* – "It's not nice to listen! You should be ashamed! Would you like it if someone listened to your conversation when you thought it was supposed to be private?"

Berel would slouch in his seat and then softly say, "I shouldn't even repeat the part they said about you?"

"Who said what?" Mama would challenge.

"The lady from upstairs – the one with the gray hair who is always yelling on us," Berel replied.

"*Nu*, so what did she say?" Mama would ask.

"You told me not to repeat – so I wouldn't repeat!" the monster replied.

"Tell me – or I'll break your neck!" Mama would scream.

Berel would smile and softly explain, "She said your honey cake wasn't as good as the lady's on the second floor."

"My honey cake!" Mama exclaimed. "What's wrong with my honey cake?"

Berel shrugged, "There's nothing wrong with it – but she said..."

We finished breakfast and went out to play ball. All the kids would cluster around Berel – just to ask him what he heard the night before. The kid was a walking newspaper.

When he ran out of stories to tell the kids – I am certain he created his own.

In fact, his descriptions of the dialogues were so inviting, I asked Mama if I could sleep with Berel in the porch room one night when it was quite hot.

"It's too hot in my room – Berel gets all the air in his!" I cried.

Once in the porch room, the antenna went up and we listened. Then I discovered that you couldn't hear a darn thing. I then realized that the monster was making up almost everything he was telling everyone.

When we went to Rockaway, we would usually go out there after the Fourth of July because we were told the rooms were cheaper. After all, the season was already underway and if someone didn't rent a room before the Fourth it was felt that the room was lost for the season. To capture whatever they could, we were told the rooming house owners gave it away for practically nothing!

We soon found out that it was a lot of baloney! Not only didn't they reduce the price of the room they would usually add a few dollars on top, expecting the customer would try to bargain them down. And sometimes when a customer didn't bargain – the landlords made the extra money. They rationalized that with the aggravation they had from renting the room, they were entitled to the little bit extra!

Rockaway in the summer was always an experience. Those were the years that very few people had enough money to go away - so we had uncles and aunts who would 'stop by' for the weekend. We always looked forward to those 'drop-ins' but to Mama it was murder. She was stuck in the kitchen a whole day and Papa was running back and forth to the store getting more groceries for our guests.

When it came time to sleep - listen, how do you cram everybody together? - it was almost like automation - they stuck five little ones into a bed - and *shoen* they were taken care of! One uncle slept in the beach chair. My aunt would sleep with Mama, and Papa would try to curl up on some makeshift couch or a set of chairs put together. No one ever got any rest on these 'sleep-outs' but who came to Rockaway for a rest? We came for a vacation - and in our way of thinking this was what a vacation was supposed to be. The only time Mama got a rest was on Monday - when she only had to prepare meals for us and do the laundry!

In the evenings, when Papa would come back from work, he would dash into the house, slip into his bathing suit and we would walk with him to the ocean so he should 'get refreshed.' We usually had a place a few blocks from the beach and by the time he walked there and back - he was as refreshed as a troop of soldiers on a forced march. But since we were in Rockaway - and a dip in the ocean was supposed to 'refresh,' Papa went every night for a swim.

Actually, we always felt it was more for show than for 'refreshment!' When he went to his place the next day he could always brag to his fellow workers that he took 'ah refreshing dip' every night and it was *ah mechayah*! (a pleasure!)

The first sunburn was always the most painful. The very first day we would go to the beach Mama would warn us - but who listened? After the sun would set and we got home - *gevald* - the shoulders burned and if there was a wind

---

on the beach and you got a wind burn – in the crease of the leg, behind the knee – you couldn't walk for days.

When sunburn struck, the remedy was simply cocoa butter or vinegar, "so it should take the sting out."

The vinegar smelled so horrible you forgot about the sting! We walked around smelling like a tossed salad – cocoa butter on the leg creases and vinegar dripping from the shoulders.

Years later they came out with fancy smelling lotions for sunburn – but who could afford them – we stayed with the vinegar and cocoa butter.

As the last few days of summer approached Mama kept marking off the calendar and breathed a sigh of relief. "Just think – school will open in one week!"

WHEN A KVITCHERER MARRIES A GRIDGERER

In our day we had two kinds of teachers: Kvitcherers (screamers) and Gridgerers. (one who gives you a dig).

I REALLY DON'T KNOW IF THEY MAKE TEACH-ers like they used to make them - when we were kids. In those years every teacher was typed. We had *kvitcherers*, hitters, and *gridgerers*. For example, if there was a teacher who screamed at kids, she was known as 'the *kvitcherer!*' (the screamer). We had a Mrs. Rosenberg who was the master *kvitcherer* of all time! On a clear day you could hear her screaming from the third floor all the way to the boiler room of the school. When she gave *ah kvitch* (a scream) the custodian would stand at attention! She was probably the prototype siren for the early warning system used in this country during the war! When she gave *a geshrie* (a yell) our hair would stand up!

Then there were 'the hitters.' These were teachers who hit! Of course, nobody ever died from it, but listen – who wanted to get hit!

Then there were the "combinationmen" – the `hitters and *kvitcherers.*' If you were unlucky enough to get one of those – in *drerd der gelt*! (forget it!) It was curtains! You got yelled at as you were being hit! Some of the kids got gray hair before they even got out of the third grade! And some even wrinkles!

There was another variety we had to look out for and those were the "humiliators." *Takeh*, we didn't call them the "humiliators" then – after all, who could spell it?

The "humiliators" would take some poor kid's homework, write a big red "D" or "UNSATISFACTORY" or "DO OVER" all over the page, then hold it up to the class – as "the example." *Gevald*! What humiliation! We knew we were stupid but who wanted to advertise it? Herby Fifelman got the business one day and actually bit Mrs. Zuckerman in the leg! *Takeh*, she had to get a tetanus shot. They figured Herby was out of his mind and maybe it was catching!

In our day, you were considered lucky if you got a teacher who was just '*ah gridgerer*!' A *gridgerer* was a teacher who started the day off with, "Who didn't do the homework?"

Some poor unfortunate soul would raise his or her hand, admit to the crime and that was it! Most teachers would talk softly, but with a *gridgerer* you got the business. She would throw in a few *gridgers* (digs) like, "Sure, then when you fail and get left back your mother will cry till she gets a breakdown!"

Or she might keep the *gridger* up all day long. For example, poor little Herby didn't know how to keep his mouth shut. Listen, the kid was friendly! So his teacher, Mrs. Lookstein would give him, "See, Herbert can talk plenty in class but when he goes home he doesn't say a word to his poor mother about homework. She scrimps and saves so he can have the best of everything, and when it comes to doing a little nothing like the homework - he has to hurt his mother."

Then she would turn to Herby and *gridger*, "Tell me, how long would it have taken you to write the fifty examples? How long? I bet the other children did it in less than six hours! How long? Herbert, you know what happens to children who don't do homework?"

Then she would pause, take a deep breath, pull out a handkerchief, and make believe she was crying and then blubber, "I just can't tell you!"

Oy, was she an actress!

Gevald! We figured Herby was a marked man! We all wanted to beat him up because of what the teacher said he was doing to his mother! The truth was his mother couldn't have cared less because she knew her Herby - when he was ready to do homework - he would do it! He always passed! The dope is now a principal!

Sometimes, when a few classes would get together in the gym, we would have a real triple-threat combination: '*ah kvitcherer,*' a 'hitter' and '*ah gridgerer.*' As little kids do, we yelled, we ran, and we were happy - but this holy triumvirate we were certain, resented the joys of youth. I am certain they did what they could to destroy us. Like Mama would say, "*fabiseners.*" (mean people). It would start out with the *kvitcherer* teacher giving a *geshrie* that would peel the paint off the walls! This would be followed by the 'hitter' who would reach for some little monster and give him a *pahtch* (a smack) on the backside. The *gridgerer* teacher would walk over silently and then begin to *gridger*, "Very nice! Very nice! You'll fall and split your head and I'll have to go to the office and fill out thirty-eight forms. Very nice - you'll get blood all over the floor and the custodian will have to call your mother to clean up the mess. Then, do you know what it will do to your mother coming down after the school is closed to get on her knees to scrub the gym floor?"

This was *a klug mutter.* (a person who always saw

tragedy).

She would paint such a graphic picture we could practically see Mama on her hands and knees scrubbing the gym floor with Mr. Murphy the custodian standing over her with the big broom he used to sweep the floor with!

We could never understand. When we went to gym we always got instructions, "You must not run! You must not yell or shout! Remember there are classes working!"

So tell me what were we supposed to do in the gym, knit a bathrobe? How do little kids play ball if they don't run or yell?

In those days they gave us exercises. You know what kind of exercises - you stood like an idiot in front of the gym while one of the triumvirate would *shtup* (push) the other to get in front of the class to be the leader for that day. We could hear them argue. The *kvitcherer* had the loudest voice and we could hear her say to one, "Sophie, it's your turn today, I got a run in my stocking yesterday when I bent down!

Then Sophie would answer, "Sarah, it's your turn! Remember I do best hitting the ones who don't do what you show them!"

Then the *gridger* teacher would comment, "I'd take it today only my mother doesn't feel well and I want to make a call to see how she feels."

This one's mother was always sick - every time she had to do something!

Herby Fifelman tried to give her the same routine one day when he didn't do homework. "My mudder is sick!" he began, "that's why I didn't do my homework - my pen scratches! She had a headache!"

And the *gridgerer* teacher would *gridger*, "No wonder she has you for *naches* (happiness) - listen, you made your mother sick."

Herby broke in with, "So who did it to your mother?"

At that point the *gridger* teacher called in the *kvitcher* for reinforcement who promptly gave Herby a lecture on respect with a scream that started in C above high C and ascended to high Z.

Don't get me wrong, we had some very normal teachers in those years - the ones who got married, became pregnant and left the school to raise a family. The only ones who were left were the *kvitcherers*, hitters and *gridgerers* - they never married. Of course, we reasoned - who wants to marry a *kvitcherer* - unless he's a hitter?

However, one year the *kvitcherer* of the third floor in charge of yelling on kids who were late, *takeh* found a mate and got married! Nu, so who would a *kvitcherer* marry? She found the perfect match! She married a teacher who worked in a nearby Talmud Torah. He was a notorious *knipper*! (pincher!) You know what a *knipper* is? That's someone who doesn't yell, *gridger*, or hit. He walks over to the side of some little monster who has committed some infraction of the rules, grabs a little piece of cheek, and gives '*ah knip*' (a pinch)! When he gave a kid '*ah knip*' - you knew you were *knipped*! You kinda wished for a hitter!

It was rumored that this *knipper* would occasionally give some kid '*ah knip*' in a place where the kid couldn't sit down for a week! But he met his match in Herby Fifelman. Herby would always have a spare peanut butter and jelly sandwich in his back pocket, just in case he ever got hungry. And Mr. Markowitz one day gave Herby a *knip* near that pocket. He wound up with a handful of peanut butter and jelly! For a minute he almost dropped dead, then he realized it was peanut butter and jelly. He thought he punctured the kid!

Nu, so the combination was good. Mrs. Rosenberg was a *kvitcherer* and Mr. Markowitz a *knipper*. You know, we actually prayed that they shouldn't have a child. Could you imagine the product of *ah knipper* and *ah kvitcherer*? But the good L-rd looked down - they were too old to have children!

You have to remember all our teachers weren't bad - we also had some wonderful compassionate teachers. I'll never forget one, Mrs. Laddowitz. This was *ah malech* (an angel). Even when a kid did something wrong, she found something nice to say. For example, the day Herby knocked over the ink bottle he used to fill the desk ink wells, Mrs. Laddowitz smiled warmly and said, "That's all right, it was an accident. Besides, the desk and the floor does look a little better in blue."

Of course she had one hell of a time trying to convince Shirley Grossman's mother that Shirley didn't sprout varicose veins at the age of 7! The ink dripped all over Shirley's feet in beautiful little streams and *takeh* – she did look like a Picasso. In those years who knew from varicose veins – we told the kids in the school Shirley went to a tattoo artist.

But today's world has changed. The *kvitcherers* are gone, along with the hitters, and the *gridgerers* all part of yesterday's world.

MAGISTRATES COURT

The old Coney Island Magistrates Court used to handle local problems in the neighborhood. But you know something - that old court had more character than a dowager Queen.

IT REALLY WASN'T THE KIND OF COURT WHERE headlines were made - it was a place where small problems were solved. It was the place where many old timers, some who could barely speak English, sought justice. The judges who sat in that old courthouse had to have more than an understanding of law - they had to know people and have the patience and wisdom of King Solomon.

You could have called it a stage on which the little people of the community played starring roles. To a spectator it was a show - a variety show. Stories of warmth, compassion, lust and crime unfolded before the bench. No writer could have created those stories. Each had its own ironic twist, often with happy endings.

Let me put it this way - it was the kind of place a tenant would drag his landlord to if he didn't give sufficient heat in the winter or no hot water in the summer. Few appeared in that court were ever really put in jail -all those who came wanted only satisfaction. Like I said, it wasn't a place for criminals. It catered to people with problems who looked to the man in the black robe for justice. I remember it was a bitter cold day and the winter snows covered the streets. The windows of the courtroom were fogged with the steam that hissed from the ancient rattling radiators that were covered with crumbling layers of silver paint.

It was the same routine for the Bridge Officer, the man who stood in front of the judge and read the formal complaints. He would pick up a paper and call out a name. On this day the bailiff brought in a shabbily dressed tired looking old man. A burly police officer sitting in the front row stepped forward and stood at the old timer's side. The threadbare clothes the old man wore told you he was a pauper. The worn tweed coat he had tightly wrapped about himself was fastened by two safety pins at the neck. That coat must have been new about twenty years before. It wasn't style the old man sought from the coat - it was warmth. The shoes that swiveled about on his feet were badly worn and still soaked from the slushy streets. They were oversized - surely not his own. He had the appearance of a clown in comic dress. But you didn't laugh.

That old timer held an old felt hat in his quivering hand. It must have been gray at one time, but now it was just a combination of sweat rings and filthy water marks. A crumpled black *yarmulke* (skull cap) covered the old man's head as he stood nervously before the judge.

The old man looked about, seemingly embarrassed as the Bridge Officer began to read the complaint. "You have been arrested and accused of theft..." the officer said.

The judge, moved by the old timer's appearance,

leaned forward on the huge mahogany desk that separated him from the defendant.

Half-smiling, half in sympathy, he asked, "Now, really what could you have stolen?"

The arresting officer took a deep breath and began, "Your honor, I caught this man stealing from a grocery..."

The judge shook his head in disbelief, then asked, "What did he steal?"

The officer said softly, "A loaf of bread..."

The judge turned to the old man and asked softly, "How old are you?"

The old timer looked up ever so pathetically and almost in a whisper said, "Seventy-eight, your honor."

"Seventy-eight," echoed the judge, "and now you're embarking on a career of crime!" He chuckled good-naturedly, hoping to relieve the tension that gripped the 'criminal' who stood before him. But the old man didn't smile back. Tears began to fill his soft brown eyes. He shook his head sadly.

The judge turned to the arresting officer sternly and snapped, "Tell us what happened..."

The officer reached into his breast pocket for a little black notebook. He fumbled with a few pages then began making a formal statement - about "being on duty on Brighton and Fourth Street..."

"No, no..." shouted the judge, "I don't want trial testimony - just tell me what happened." He seemed almost impatient.

The police officer explained that he saw the old timer leaving the market with a loaf of bread under his coat. He said that he walked up to the old man and asked him if he had paid for the bread. He said that the old man then admitted the theft.

"He confessed your honor...yes sir - he confessed!" the officer proudly exclaimed.

There was a silence in the courtroom that told you a great drama was yet to unfold. Even the clunking radiators seemed hushed at this moment.

The judge leaned forward, stared at the old man for a moment and asked softly, "Why didn't you pay for the bread?"

The old man brushed away the tears that had begun to run down his cheeks and in a quivering voice replied, "I was...hungry."

He lowered his eyes to the floor and almost apologetically continued. "I had money... but I accidentally dropped it in the snow on the way to the store." He looked at the officer who stood at his side and continued, "It was all the money I had left."

The judge asked, "Are you on welfare?"

The old man stiffened up indignantly and almost shouted, "No - why should I? I can still work! G-d will help me - I'll find work soon and pay the store for the bread."

The judge smiled helplessly, "But that wouldn't change anything - you admitted to committing a crime and the law says I have to punish you...it makes no exceptions."

The old man stared at the judge helplessly and shrugged in embarrassment. "I'm sorry to have caused so much trouble...I really didn't steal - I've lived with G-d too many years to betray him now." He looked pensively toward the ceiling of the courtroom and continued. "This must have been G-d's way to punish me for my selfishness..."

"Your selfishness?" asked the judge. "How were you selfish?"

The old man smiled humbly and nodding his head almost as if in prayer, "I thought of myself - rather than to pray to G-d for help. The hunger would have passed and this never would have happened." The tears came once more. "I deserve the punishment your honor - I deserve it!"

The judge sat solemnly. He tried to hold back tears - but his eyes filled. He cleared his throat in a business- like fashion and said, "Nevertheless, you admitted to committing a crime and I am bound by law to impose a punishment. He hesitated for a moment, "That will be ten dollars or ten days in jail!"

A hush fell over the courtroom. What a travesty – where would he get ten dollars? He didn't even have the few cents for the bread!

At that moment the judge stood up, reached into his back pocket for his wallet, took out a ten dollar bill and handed it to the court clerk. "Here, this should cover it!"

When the old man saw this he called out in embarrassment, "Oh, please your honor – it is my punishment – not yours. You have the law to uphold. You shouldn't."

But the judge ignored the plea. He turned toward the courtroom spectators who looked at him with smiles of admiration. Then, in a commanding shout he ordered, "And furthermore, I'm going to fine everyone in this courtroom fifty cents for the opportunity of seeing and hearing a breed of man that is all but lost to our generation."

He turned to the bailiff and commanded, "Bailiff, collect the fines and give them to the defendant!"

The bailiff smiled back knowingly and walked among the attorneys, their clients and spectators with a borrowed hat. Most gave a dollar, some five, and even ten. Everyone in the courtroom knew what the judge meant.

The old man clutched his coat tightly shaking his head in bewilderment, "Please your honor – no, no, it's not right – why punish them also...please..."

But the judge didn't listen and the bailiff continued to collect the 'fines.' When he had reached each person in the courtroom he returned to the judge's bench, dumped the money on a table and counted it.

Every face in that courtroom had a smile on it – even the landlords who were dragged in for not giving enough heat. The old man kept shuffling back and forth perplexed, saying "It isn't right...I am the one to be punished..."

After the money had been counted the judge turned to the old timer and said, "Didn't you say G-d would help?"

The old timer shook his head.

"And so he did..." replied the judge softly. "Since a few

cents was all you had left, maybe it was G–d who made you lose the money in the snow? Maybe, he let you put that loaf of bread under your coat to be caught by the officer who brought you here so that we could help."

The old man began to smile uneasily. Then his face lit up as he realized an inner thought. He began to nod and a twinkle filled his eyes. He breathed a sigh of relief and said, "Maybe you're right, your honor – maybe you're right." He emphasized each word carefully. "But could I give some of this money to some poor people I know? They have children to feed."

The judge's eyes filled with tears as he turned away to fill out the papers before him. Looking at the complaint sheet he called out, "Officer, you didn't put down your name or precinct number on the complaint sheet." As he looked up the officer was gone – he was no longer at the old man's side.

"Where's the officer who brought this man in?" shouted the judge. "See if he's in the hallway." The bailiff ran out into the hallway but the officer had vanished.

The judge looked up from his desk and a strange smile crossed his face. The judge shook his head and laughing to himself said, "No...no, it couldn't be...it couldn't be, no one could vanish like that officer – and his name isn't even on the records – this can't happen." The judge's smile broke into a hearty laughter. "Maybe? Maybe? Who can tell?" he shrugged, "We're all G–d fearing men.".

The old timer didn't join in the laughter, but raised his eyes toward the ceiling once more and moved his lips silently. He then turned toward the judge and sighed, "Judge...you have the wisdom of King Solomon..." He lowered his eyes, turned slowly toward the door and shuffled down the center aisle of the courtroom that led to the street.

That old timer didn't know how right he was – because the judge who was on the bench was the late Magistrate, Judge Charles Solomon – a man who tempered law with compassion.

THINGS WE REMEMBER BEST

There are some things from our youth we can never forget. They weren't really important things but we can never forget them.

I WAS JUST THINKING, THERE ARE SO MANY wonderful memories everyone of us has. In fact, someone asked me if there was any one memory that stood out in my mind from when I was a kid.

The one thing that really stood out in my mind was how we took lunch to school during Passover holidays. I'll never forget how Mama would make us *hock fleish* sandwiches with two pieces of matzos. First she would smear the matzos quite liberally with chicken *schmaltz*, sprinkle it with salt, and then gently press the hunk of *hock fleish* in between the two slices of matzos. As we walked to the subway to go to school, the chicken *schmaltz* would start to melt and by the time we reached the subway platform it was leaking through the brown paper bag.

I'll never forget when my little brother Berel would walk to school and *schlep* his brown paper bag of *hock fleish* sandwiches. The chicken *schmaltz* would melt and he would leave a trail of chicken *schmaltz* for blocks. In fact, every cat and dog in the neighborhood would come out of hiding and follow him to school. Sometimes, Mama would also slip in a few pieces of sliced onion to give it a real kick. I want you to know you could have smelled that kid two blocks away. When he got to school, the teacher would ask him to put his lunch on the window sill and then open the window even if it was below zero outside!

Sometimes Mama would put in a nice big tomato for me when I was going to high school so the lunch shouldn't be dry. But I had to take a subway to Evander Childs High School in the Bronx. So when I got on the train, If a fat lady sat down next to me, inevitably she would squeeze into a space that a midget couldn't even fit into and squash the tomato. One woman nearly who squeezed her way next to me nearly fainted when she saw tomato juice running down her leg. She was convinced one of the toothpicks Mama enclosed in the bag had stabbed her to death.

Passover stood out in my mind because I will never forget the thermos bottles we had in those years that we took to school with our lunch. When we had a *fleishika* lunch, Mama would put some plain seltzer and some orange juice in a thermos bottle so our lunch shouldn't be dry. But walking around a whole day with that thermos bottle was an adventure. When lunch time came and we started to remove the cork from the thermos, the seltzer would shoot out of the thermos like it was champagne!

Another thing that stood out in my mind was buying a suit for us when we were kids. Mama was raised on the Lower East Side of New York. So when it came to getting a suit for my Bar Mitzvah, the folks got in touch with a cousin who was supposed to be the suit *maven*. He too was brought up on the Lower East Side so he took us downtown to buy a suit for me. As we walked down Stanton Street, the boys clothing store owners and their salesmen would be standing outside their store looking for possible customers. If they saw a lady and two men with a kid that looked about 13 years old, they knew they had a possible customer. The owner would run inside the store, pick up a dark navy blue suit and call out to Mama, "Missus, please excuse me. My eyes aren't so good. Is this a navy blue, or is this a black?"

Listen what could be wrong in helping out this poor soul? So Mama would look at the material, smile to the store owner or salesman and say, "I think it's really a very dark navy blue."

The salesman would smile and be so apologetic. "Thank you so much. I'm so sorry I interrupted you. By the way I would like to return the favor if you are looking for *ah* suit for the young man."

Listen, an offer like that you just don't pass up. So before anyone knew what was going on the folks inside the store and the salesman was showing us his merchandise. That's the way it was when we were kids.

And another thing we didn't have to have R-rated or even X-rated movies in our day to have people go to the movies. We had something better. It was called "Dish Night." In those days, to encourage people to go to the movies during the middle of the week, the neighborhood theaters would give out a dish to every woman who went in after five in the afternoon. The purpose was to make the people come to the movies regularly. If you did, you wound up with a beautiful set of dishes. The only problem was, sometimes they would have a movie that Mama and Papa did not care to see so they would go to a theater other than the one they usually went to. That theater also gave out a different style of dish. It was usually a very pretty pattern but in a different color and design from the one given out by the other theater. So Mama saved those dishes and they became the *passadicker* dishes. And when *pesach* came the table looked like an explosion in a gut factory with all the different color dishes.

I'll never forget how Mama used to get the Passover *Hagadahs*. This was the height of the depression period so when Mama placed her order with the grocery man, she always got *hagadahs*. Remember those *Hagadahs* with the Maxwell House coffee advertisement on the back. In fact, when we were kids, we figured Maxwell House coffee was part of the Passover seder. We figured when Moses was walking out of Egypt and was in the desert he stopped occasionally for a cup of Maxwell House coffee.

You know what I really find disturbing? Today's telephones. The other day we called up a movie theater to find out what time the movie started. So the theater had one of those answering machines connected to their phone. When it answered it said, "Press 1, if you want to know what is playing. Press 2, if you want to know who's in the movie. Press 3 if you want to reach the porter. Press 4…" what kind of business is this? What was so terrible about having a person answer the phone to give you the information?

You know what probably happened, so many people when they were away from home and wanted to let their parents know they arrived safely, they would call home, person to person and ask for themselves.

And what did we have to entertain ourselves when we were kids? The girls had horse reins and boys had baseball tickets. Remember the horse reins the girls used to make? They would spend a whole summer making that snake-like material with the hope of turning it into a rug. My sisters actually made a rug out of horse reins, then they wouldn't let anybody walk on it.

The boys played with the baseball cards that are worth a fortune today. You know what's also worth alot of money? The covers from Reid's ice cream dixie cups with the pictures of the movie stars. Remember those?

And how about the diseases we had in our day? We

didn't have antibiotics or even vitamins to stay healthy. We had something better. We had little camphor bags Mama would hang around our neck. Some parents hung little garlick bags on their kids. The camphor or the garlick bags were supposed to keep us disease free. If you had a garlick bag, you always got a seat on the subway. If you wore a camphor bag, you smelled like a coat that had been hung in the closet all summer long.

We didn't have the conveniences they have today. Papa would attach an orange crate we got from the fruit store. Mama would put all the fruits and vegetables in that box and the stuff would stay fresh. Those were the days that for fifteen cents or a quarter you had the ice man put ice in the ice box. And don't think those ice boxes didn't build character for us kids. One kid in the family was appointed the *shissel* emptier. This kid had to empty the *shissel* twice a day. If we forgot, our neighbor who lived in the apartment under us would take her broom and knock on her ceiling and yell, "Mrs. Fine, *ess rint foon dir.*"

In our day we had all kinds of entertainment. We even had better stereo than they have today. On a sunday morning, all the radios in our building were tuned to the Forvetz Hour on WEVD. People left their windows open so the neighbors who didn't have a radio could hear. Remember Michel Livitzky and the News?

We didn't have blue cross in those days either. Do you realize for what it costs to be sick one day today we could have been sick for a whole year when we were kids.

We had neighbors who came to the rescue of every family. If a woman's son was going to school to learn how to be a doctor, it was assumed she knew about medicine. If a woman's son was going to law school, she became a consultant when a legal question came up. Listen it was a different world.

THE SMELLS IN OUR DAY

When we were kids, smells had become a very important part of our generation. We fought disease with smells and savored the smell of fresh bread.

Our generation was always surrounded by a variety of smells. First of all, in our day, to prevent us from catching any disease, we didn't have to take shots from doctors. Mama had her own remedy that was imported from Europe. She would sew up a little bag with camphor and tie it around our necks with a shoe lace. That home remedy was supposed to ward off any disease that might even dare to venture near our body.

I really don't know what the camphor bags did, but the truth is, we rarely ever got sick. In fact, if my memory serves me correctly, our generation had a lot less disease than today's generation. Who knew from flu or flu shots? If you got sick in the winter it was simply called a cold. If someone died from the cold everyone thought they had, the druggist would say "Apparently it was not a cold but a virus." Of course, nobody knew what a virus was in those years and kept marveling about new medical discoveries.

Some parents would use a double whammy to protect their children. Mostly the Italian parents used this method. They would make their kids wear the camphor bag around their neck, plus depending on what diseases were going around, they would hang a few pieces of garlick around a kid's neck. True, with a garlic bag around your neck you always got a seat on the subway. If you had a camphor bag and a garlic bag around your neck, you got the whole car. If you were a girl you could be certain no male would even think about making a pass at you. To my knowledge, not one girl I ever knew from school, who wore a camphor bag around her neck was ever attacked by anyone. So you see the old time preventatives really did work.

Listen, in those years camphor was a big thing. When my sisters went to school they smelled like a coat that had been hanging in the closet all summer long with camphor balls still in the pockets. Mama was a big believer in camphor. She was also a big believer in kerosene. Kerosene? For what? Let me explain, in those years, my sisters had long hair. This was also a time when it was said some kids in school had nits in their hair. So Mama in her infinite wisdom of old world remedies, use to wash my sisters' hair on the average of once or twice a week, then rinse the hair with kerosene and water. Then she would comb it out with a fine toothed comb. After that treatment my sisters would walk around the neighborhood smelling like ah house painter.

We were always surrounded by smells. In the hallways, on a Friday afternoon, when we came home from school, the whole building smelled from fresh challah. Everybody was baking either a cake or bread. Let me tell you something, there was one smell that always managed to appear on

Thursday. That was the day most women used to render their chicken fat. In order to reduce the horrible odor the melting fat made, women used to cut in onions. The addition of the onions made that terrible smell more acceptable. The by-product of that effort was called *gribines*. Let me tell you something if you can't afford oil or gas to heat your home in the winter, try eating a few *gribines*! I guarantee, the fires will be lit in the stomach. Don't get me wrong *gribines* are delicious, but you better have a stomach that could handle it or quick access to a stomach pump.

Chicken fat was a very important ingredient in those years. Jewish cooking demanded the use of chicken fat with almost every type of meat dish that was being made. In fact, a fast food delicacy in those years, was a crust of pumpernickel, liberally smeared with chicken fat on the soft side of the bread. After the fat soaked into the bread, we would rub the bread crust with a clove of garlic. Then we would sprinkle kosher salt on the crust. I want you to know *ut* was a delicacy!

Between you and me, I think doctors invented chicken fat to load up an entire generation with cholseterol that they would eventually treat. Listen, we ate that glop for years, now they tell us we were poisoning ourselves. They didn't say a word about *gribiness* that was mixed into chopped liver. Never a word in those years. But now, when a visit to a doctor is more than $20 they tell us we were poisoning ourselves and only they know how to get rid of the cholesterol clogging up the arteries. Now they tell us!

Say what you want about the crazy eating habits of our generation because today's generation is just as bad. Incidentally, if you really want to have an old world delicacy experience without the cholesterol, just get the crust of a rye bread or a pumpernickel and rub the end crust with a garlic clove. Let it stand for about two minutes then sprinkle on a little salt. I want you to know the mouth sings! True, nobody goes near you for two days and you are guaranteed a seat on the subway, but that is a delicious food experience especially if you know somebody who had to put on weight.

Smell also plays an important part in today's generation. Today my wife has little bowls of dead flowers all over the house. It is called potpourri or sachet. This is suppose to make the house smell nice. To tell the truth sometimes when my wife buys certain brands, it makes the house smell like the mens' room at Radio City Music Hall.

At one time my wife used to buy all kinds of pretty smelling stuff that came in a can. Then she read that the aerosol gas in the can was destroying the environment so she stopped using the spray can stuff. In fact, I used to have a can of shaving cream that would last me about two or three months. I would press a little button on the can and the foaming soap would come out. When my wife found out the propellant in the can was aerosol, she made me stop using the canned soap.

We used to get into the most heated arguments. I would argue, "You mean to tell me the one or two seconds I hold down the lever of this can will release enough aerosol to cause harm to the atmosphere?"

And she would snap back, "Yes! True, you use it for one or two seconds, but the fellow next door uses it for one or two seconds and the fellow next door to him uses it for one or two seconds. Then, before you know it there are hours and hours of aerosol being released into the air. In no time it will tear away the protective layer that protects us from the sun."

I was angry. "If that's such a big concern, protecting us from the sun, how come in the winter when we go for a walk, you always make me walk on the sunny side of the street. And then in the summer we sit at the beach in the sun, with our whole body smeared with sun shield."

My wife is an excellent arguer. "The doctors found out that too much sun causes skin problems," she exclaimed.

"Great, so why even sit in the sun? Why don't we just sit in the house? We paid a small fortune for air conditioners all over the house. So what happens the minute the summer arrives? You want to run to the beach to broil under a sun because you have on the sun shield lotion. where's the logic to all this?"

Right away an argument. So she bought me an electric shaving machine. "Okay, let me ask you," I began. "Now that I have an electric shaving machine that runs on electricity, doesn't the electric company have to burn extra coal or oil to provide extra electricity for me to run the electric razor? If we're so concerned with the environment, how come we're making the electric company use more electricity which has to be made with some kind of fossil fuel because atomic energy is too dangerous?"

Any way you look at it we're stuck. I love my wife dearly because she always has an answer for everything. Whether it's the right answer or not, she's got an answer. In the house she never corrects me. For example, if I should do some shopping and come home, I might say "Wow, it was really crowded in the supermarket. There must have been a million people at the checkout counter."

She would not say a word. However, when we're with company and if I should say, "...do you believe the prices on food today? Just last week when I went to the supermarket, there must have been a million people at the checkout counter."

Suddenly my wife comes alive. Then addressing everyone who is listening, she would say, "There weren't a million people at the checkout line, maybe three or four people were before us."

So when we get home, I'd ask her, "Why did you have to mix in when I said there were a million people in front of me at the supermarket?"

Then she'll turn to me and with a look encompassing the innocents of a new born baby and say, "I mixed in? What did I have to do with it? You were telling a story and you simply exaggerated. I don't want people to think you exaggerate when you tell a story. I must have told you a million times not to exaggerate!"

Shoen! The Wizard hath spoken.

A short time ago a fellow wrote a book and I think the title was, "Everything I Needed to Know, I Learned in Kindergarten." So I said to my wife, "Was that fellow exaggerating? Didn't he have to go to college to learn how to write the book?

She turned away and then raised her nose in the air with, "That is simply an expression. He realized it was an exaggeration because it was a catchy title."

So if I said there were a million people ahead of me in the supermarket, wasn't that an expression of exaggeration to capture the interest of the people who were listening?"

"How can you compare writing a book to shopping in a supermarket," she snapped back.

"Okay," I came back at her. "Why is it whenever I go to the supermarket with you and you pick out the basket that we have to wheel around the store as we select the groceries, you always manage to take the wagon that has the square wheel? How come? Huh? And isn't it true, I always get stuck with pushing that stupid wagon? You know what happens when we buy soda that has been bouncing around in that wagon with the flat wheel, the soda is so shook up by the time we get home I can't open the bottle for at least a week without it fizzing up all over the place as soon as the cap is flipped off."

"So who tells you to drink soda? Watsamatter, water isn't healthier?"

Listen, I'm convinced, you can't win an argument today.

KEEPING COOL
DURING THE SUMMER

Let me tell you something. When we were kids we learned how to fight the hot weather. In those days, only if you had the money could you afford an electric fan. So takeh how did we manage to survive in the simmering heat we also had in those years?

We couldn't even afford a fan in those depression years. I remember Mama had little ventilator screens that fit at the bottom of the window. They were supposed to allow fresh air into the apartment and keep out flies or bugs. The truth is, those ventilators allowed the flies and mosquitoes into the apartment, but it sure made it difficult for them to get out. We became 'free lunch' for those little critters.

In our day the only place in the neighborhood that had air-conditioning was the good old Chester Theater which was located at Tremont Avenue and Boston Post Road in the Bronx. On a real hot day we would go to the Chester and amble toward the lobby of the theater. We would stand there and wait for people to come out. Every time someone opened a door to leave, we would get a blast of that cool air.

The other theaters in the Bronx would hang a sort of piece of canvas on their marquee with a picture of a Polar Bear sitting on an iceberg. And in big letters a sign read, "COOL INSIDE." The implication was that the theater had air-conditioning. But the smaller theaters only had fans on the side of the auditorium that hummed so loud you could barely hear what the actors and actress were saying on the screen.

In the evening, the Vogue Theater on Daly Avenue advertised, "Keep Cool On Our Roof-Garden Theater." The roof-garden theater was the roof of the theater. When it was really hot, the theater would have their projectionist bring a movie projector to the roof of the theater where there would be hard wooden benches that you sat on to watch the movie in the open air. Since it was dark at night, you sat on the roof of the theater and the mosquitoes had a ball. The people who lived in the house next to the movie used to put a few blankets on the fire escape and watch free movies. They really couldn't hear to well but they saw free movies.

As the years passed and air-conditioners came out for the home, the coolest place we could go was to the appliance store on Tremont Avenue called Ritz Radio. They would have radios and phonographs and when air-conditioning came out they made that store nice and cool.

Then the Woolworth Five and Ten store on Tremont Avenue put in air conditioning. We would go into that store with our big ten or fifteen cents and spend half the day cooling off.

In our neighborhood, the fire department used to take a big pipe on a stand, place it in a school yard and connect it to a hydrant. They would turn the water on and it would run all day long. That water was ice cold. We would put on a bathing suit, grab a towel and sit in the school yard near that shower. When we got real hot, we would run through the shower and cool off. That was our 'swimming pool' in those days.

During those hot summer nights most of the neighbors would take a folding chair or a milk box from the grocery store and sit in front of the house and shmooze. We kids would sit on the stoop and play a game called "Actors and Actresses." The actors and actresses in those years were so well known that all we had to do was mention their initials and we would know who they were talking about. For example, one kid would say, "G.C. an actor."

We would think for a moment then say "Gary Cooper."

Then the next kid might say "J.G., actress."

We'd think for a few minutes and then say, "Janet Gaynor."

And that's how it went. We kept cool. Every so often the Bungalow Bar truck would come down the street which meant we would run to Mama or Papa for a nickle for a pop or a fudgical. Sometimes an ices man and his little pushcart would come around and we could buy a cup of ices for three cents any flavor.

Those were the summer months. Sometimes, if the men wanted to play cards, they would bring a bridge table up to the roof and someone would run a very long extension cord from their apartment to the roof. They would plug in a lamp and sit down and play cards in the open air.

The women would bring up chairs and some blankets that the kids could sit on. The radios in those years were so huge you couldn't possibly bring one up to the roof. Later on, when smaller sets came out, radios were brought up to the roof and we would listen to music from Ben Marden's Riviera in New Jersey or the Glen Island Casino where all the big bands played. Listen, we made do and entertained ourselves.

Papa worked in a shop in the garment center where they had a pressing machine and the temperature in that place was always at least forty to fifty degrees hotter than it was in the city. I went up to visit him one time and it was like working in a blast furnace.

In our day there were no refrigerators so the mainstay for keeping food cool was the iceman. He would come down the street with his wagon and chip away at the huge blocks of ice. If you ordered a twenty-five cent piece of ice you got a piece about one foot by one foot. A thiry-five cent piece of ice was a little larger. As kids we would always hang around the ice wagon in the hopes that a small piece of ice would fall off so we could hold it to our head to cool off.

An ice box in those years, where food and milk was kept from spoiling, had a *shissel* under it. This was a pan to catch the ice drippings. The *shissel* had to be emptied two or three times in a day or else it would run over and consequently down to the apartment below. The fancier houses had a pipe that would catch the drippings that would lead into a sewer. Most houses did not have this convenience. So the first order a kid got as he was growing up was, "Empty the *shissel!*"

I did it, my sisters did it and my little brother Berel had to do it. Each looked forward to this job, but after a while it became a chore and if we'd forget, we would get yelled at by Mama. Not only did Mama give us the business but Mama's neighbor, Mrs. Mermelstein, who lived beneath us would start to bang on her ceiling to our apartment and yell, "Mrs. Fine, *ess gist by deer!*"

That would be Mama's cue to look under the ice box and see if the shissel was over-flowing. She would make her apologies to Mrs. Mermelstein and scream at us for not emptying the shissel.

In those years, not everything went into the ice box because everything couldn't fit. The next best thing was the window box. Papa would get an orange crate from the fruit store, attach a few wires to it and hang it outside the kitchen window. In that box Mama usually put the vegetables and some fruits. It really wasn't much cooler in that box than the outside air, but in the evenings when it would cool off, the stuff in that box also got cool. Listen, it wasn't the greatest way to keep food fresh, but we managed to survive.

One of the events of those years, when it was terribly hot, was, from time to time, a horse would collapse in the street from the heat. It was such a pity to see those beautiful animals lying on their side, gasping for air. The owner of the horse drawn wagon would be very concerned and he would lie down next to his horse and ask people to bring out pots of cold water. He would gently pour the cool water over the horse's head and then try to wet down the horse's body. Sometimes the horse would catch its breath and stand up after the owner would unhook the harness from the wagon. Other times, the horse just passed away. When that happened, someone would call the Sanitation Department. They would send a truck with a winch and chains and pull the horse into the truck to be carted off. It was such a pity. The owners would cry and it was so unusual to see the wagon parked on the street with no horse. We often wondered how the poor soul every got home, and how he got the wagon back to its stable?

One way some of the old timers would keep cool in those years, and we never understood it, was to drink a glass of extremely hot tea. Those old timers would claim the tea cooled them off! They would put a piece of sugar in their mouth and as the tea ran over the sugar it sweetened it. I could never understand it. I tried it once, burned my tongue and never tried it again.

When cars started to have air-conditioners, I'll never forget a *knocker* who used to live in our old neighborhood. His car didn't have air-conditioning. To make the neighbors think he was doing well and that he could afford an air conditioner in his car this nut, on the hottest days, would ride around with his windows closed. Every so often he would wipe the sweat from his brow and look as cool as if he really had air-conditioning. But, we knew. He didn't fool anybody.

I'll never forget when the first refrigerators came out and some of the people had to pay an increase in their rent to get one. The first refrigerators in our neighborhood were Kelvenators and ran on gas. If you came into an apartment that had a Kelvenator refrigerator, and you went into the kitchen, boy was it hot. But those gas refrigerators worked beautifully. Of course, most of the time you couldn't sit in the kitchen on a hot summer's day. In the winter those things were a pleasure. It kept the kitchen nice and warm.

Later on, the Electralux refrigerators began appearing and they ran on electricity. The Frigidaire Company came out with their refrigerator and before long almost every home had a refrigerator. When that took place, people kept coming down to the street with pitchers of ice water. They were so proud to make their own ice. Sometimes they would put a little orange juice in with the water they put in the ice cube trays and we would have something to suck on in those steaming hot nights. It also kept the kids busy.

Regardless of how hot it was in those years, the men still wore long pants and the women full length dresses. There was a certain dignity connected to our generation's elders. Today, it's a different story.

On those hot summer nights I remember Mama used to make a 'fruit soup.' She would buy fruit that was close to spoiling. The fruit man was only too glad to move it off his shelf for a fraction of its original cost. Mama would wash the fruit, cook it, and then let it sit in the refrigerator or the ice box. And it was really a cool delicious meal with a piece of pumpernickle. Incidentally, remember the big pumpernickle company in those years, Stuhmers Pumpernickle?

Today it's a new world with air- conditioners and yet everybody is complaining about the heat. They go from an air-conditioned house to an air-conditioned car to an air-conditioned office. So its hot. Listen what did we expect in the summer, snow storms? Wait, wait as the winter approaches, you'll be thinking of those summer days as the snow piles up around us.

THE PEOPLE WHO IMPRESSED US

Over here there should be an introductory paragraph

Did you ever stop to think of the people who impressed you most when you were a little kid? They really weren't important people but you can never forget them. For example, remember how important we thought the ticket taker at the movies was? You would purchase your ticket and the ticket taker was always dressed in a military-type uniform that included a military -type cap like General MacArthur wore. He would stand in the lobby next to the door that gave you entrance to the theater auditorium, take your ticket, tear it in half and allow you to enter. Wow, did we think he was important!

How about the kid in school who always got a hundred on the spelling test? Remember that kid? It was always a girl. *Oy* did she impress me. No matter how much I studied, I could never get a hundred. This girl always got a hundred. Remember how the teacher would praise her to the sky? Milty Foreman and myself, in spelling, always had average grades in the mid sixties. We considered that a gentleman's grade. And why not? We had our own philosophy. We really felt anybody who would spell a word twice the same way lacked a certain amount of originality!

I could never understand why our teacher made such a big *t'zimmis* when we spelled the word "receive." Milty and I were traditionalists. We figured if you spelled the word "believe" what was wrong with spelling the word "receive" the same way — "recieve?" The teacher tried to drum into our heads the rule 'i' before 'e' except after 'c.'" Big deal! If we spelled it with the "e" before the "i" anybody could still tell it was the word receive. But you should see the big commotion she made if we spelled it wrong. *Oy* did she carry on! I think she took it personally.

Oh, you know who also impressed me when I was in elementary school? The kid who was designated as the "principal's monitor." *Ut* was a job! This was usually a kid in one of the brighter classes who would be given the honor of sitting in the principal's office for an hour or so to deliver messages to teachers all over the building. In those days there were no intercoms or speaker systems in the schools, so if the principal had to get a special message to a teacher, this kid did the delivery.

It was usually a girl who wore a spotless white middy blouse, red tie and a blue skirt. They gave her a purple sash to wear over her shoulder, you know like the kind Miss America wears, that said, "Principal's Monitor." That was class! This kid had the run of the whole school. When she would enter a room, the teacher would practically snap to attention. Listen, this was a message from the principal! It was like delivering a message from Garcia, (whoever he was).

After school, when we walked home, the kids would

point at the principal's monitor and whisper to each other, like she was a Hollywood celebrity — "That's the principal's monitor!" *Gevald* did we think that kid was important.

Talk about teachers impressing you, I'll never forget one teacher in our school who really impressed me — she was the teacher who played the march music when we marched into the assembly. On Assembly Day, which was usually a Friday, every boy had to wear a white shirt, red tie and blue pants. The girls had to wear their white middy blouse, red tie and blue pleated skirt. That was the uniform. If we came, *ga'fa'bit* with a blue shirt, or even grey pants, or a blue tie instead of red, we were told horrible things happened to such kids. Actually kids who violated the dress code would be placed at the end of the line and made to sit in the back of the auditorium to await their fate.

Getting back to the teacher who played the piano, she would play an exciting Sousa march on that piano that sounded like a real military band. When we were supposed to sing "The Star Spangled Banner," she would give one chord on the piano. That meant everybody had to stand. We would stand, face the flag, and say the Pledge of Allegiance. Then she would give two chords on the piano. That was the signal for us to sing "The Star Spangled Banner." She played that piano with such force it was really stirring.

One day when one of the kids who was in the color guard got sick, and I was chosen to be his substitute, I got to the auditorium early. This teacher was at the piano practic-ing. Thinking she was alone in the auditorium, she began to play one of the popular songs of the day. I was aghast! A teacher playing a popular song in our auditorium! *Gevald!* For us little kids, that auditorium was almost sacred! *Oy* was I impressed! Listen, in our day teachers were one step away from G-d! Would G-d play a popular song?

I'll never forget another teacher in our school who really impressed me as a kid. This was the teacher who was in charge of the crossing guards. In those years, at the beginning of each term, the oldest kids in the school were selected to be school crossing guards. This was some honor! They gave you a white sash belt with a beautiful chromium arm band that said, "AAA - School Crossing Guard." The kids chosen to be the guards were trained by this teacher. Four or five kids were always trained as substitutes, just in case any of the crossing guards got sick. You were sort of an understudy. We used to pray that one of them got sick so we could take over, but it seldom happened. Anyway, this teacher would take us out of class, in our coats, to the street corner. She would walk with one kid to the middle of the street and say, "When the children come out of the building you take up your post and hold you hands up to stop the traffic till the children cross. You are in charge!"

Gevald! What authority! We could actually hold up traffic!

I'll never forget how the local police officer who walked the beat near the school came over to her one day and smiled. Wow, were we impressed! She even called that cop by his first name. That really impressed us! Then we found out he was her brother. We nearly passed out. What a connection!

There was another fellow who always impressed me as a little kid. This was the fellow who walked the aisles in the shul during the high holidays and kept banging on a book to command silence. He would give any kid who was talking a dirty look followed by a scowl, slamming the palm of his hand on his prayer book and in a stage whisper, shout, "Children! Sharrup da mouth."

Everybody respected him because he had the keys to the shul's front door and could open the shul when the rabbi was not available. He was an old timer, but his freedom to walk around and even say a word or two to the other old timers while the rabbi spoke, that was impressive.

In our day there were dozens of kosher butcher shops in our neighborhood and when we would hear Mama and her friends discussing what they were making for supper, we were always so impressed with our butcher. Mama used to say, "My butcher gave me a piece of flank'n that is pure gold. I also got a piece of *helz'l* for some *kishkeh* that was perfect."

The other women would always complain that their butcher never really gave them the good stuff and they admitted that Mama's butcher was *takeh* the best in the neighborhood. The fact that they admitted our butcher was so superior really impressed me. When Mama would take me shopping with her I would look at this man in his blood stained apron with awe.

Our janitor was also a man who impressed me. He was a strong burly gentleman who would swing the garbage cans loaded with ashes like they were nothing. That was impressive. He would walk around the building like it was his own. On rainy days we would play in the hall. If he would see us he would give a *geshrie*, "This hall is no playground!" And we would run back to our apartment. He impressed us with his commanding tone.

During the summer Mama used to have an ice man who filled the ice box with ice a few times a week. This was an old Italian man who in the summer used to put a heavy cake of ice on his shoulder, which was covered with a large piece of carpeting or burlap, carry the ice up three flights of stairs, and always with a smile, put the ice in the ice box. He would chip off a small piece of ice and hand it to us to munch on as we watched in wonder. This was a fellow who impressed us. After he would leave, Mama would mention to one of our neighbors that our ice man was the best in the neighborhood because he had a son who was going to college! In those years that was impressive.

We had a neighbor who also impressed us. She had a son who was going to medical school to study to be a doctor. If anybody in the building ever got sick, she was the first one they would call. They figured, listen, if she had a son who was going to be a doctor, she certainly had to know something about medicines. She was the chief consultant in the building. If they wanted a second opinion they would call on Mrs. Mermelstein whose brother was a pharmacist. They figured she too, had to have some medical knowledge with a brother who owned a drug store. Till this very day Mermelstein impresses me!

As a kid, I always felt our old building had the top consultants in the neighbrohood. If it came to investments, there was Mr. Rabinowitz who was the chief consultant. We were told he worked on Wall Street. When his name was mentioned, *takeh* people would stop and listen. The fact is Rabinowitz worked as a runner on Wall Street for a small brokerage firm. He probably knew less about the stock market than our butcher, but he was the chief consultant. When people would discuss the economic condition of the nation it would always be prefixed by, "Rabinowitz says..." and that was the most authoritative source anyone could give.

Rabinowitz was quite a character. He would tell ten people a certain stock was going to move up and another ten people it was going down. In a month he had ten friends regardless of which direction the stock went. He would do this all the time and people would swear by his judgment. Listen, he impressed everyone.

There was another old timer who really impressed me and that was Mama's laundry man. This was an old timer who had a small wagon pulled by a very old, tired looking horse. Whenever he would come to pick up laundry he would sigh that his old horse was feeling its years. He would tell Mama how he would massage the horses leg with linament every night and how he literally shivered over that horse. He would let us pet the horse as it stood at the curb. It was a big old horse who *shlepped* that laundry wagon around the neighborhood for years. It knew the stops in front of each house. That old laundryman and his horse were part of our early culture that taught us a love for animals. Gosh, that old man really loved animals.

There were authority figures who impressed us or maybe they intimidated us in those years, but there was always a quality that made an imprint on our young minds. As we grew older, those seemingly important people sort of drifted into oblivion and new ones took their place.

Till this very day, I'm always impressed by an accountant. They write such tiny, neat little figures in those tiny little spaces. I could never get more than three numbers in those little boxes.

I'm impressed by educators who write in the good old fashioned English, and do not use words that send you running to a dictionary to find out what they are really saying.

I'm impressed by *menchlachkiet*, when a person is decent and has compassion on his fellow man.

I am impressed by people in authority who do not misuse that authority and mete out justice with a humanism.

I guess most of us share those feelings. I guess the answer lies in respect. If we respect someone, they impress us. Do you agree?

A judge was listening to the complaints of a woman whose husband was seeking a divorce. She believed he was unfaithful to her. The judge asked, "From what you tell me, madam, I might as well give your husband a divorce. Is that agreeable to you."

What shouted the woman, "I lived with this nut for twenty years, and now I should make him happy? Never!"